The Fundamental Particles

This book is in the

ADDISON-WESLEY SERIES IN PHYSICS

The Fundamental Particles

CLIFFORD E. SWARTZ

State University of New York, Stony Brook

ADDISON-WESLEY PUBLISHING COMPANY, INC.

READING, MASSACHUSETTS

539.72 /
S973 f

Copyright © 1965

ADDISON-WESLEY PUBLISHING COMPANY, INC.

Printed in the United States of America

Library of Congress Catalog Card No. 65-10929

Philippines Copyright 1965

BY ADDISON-WESLEY PUBLISHING COMPANY, INC.

ADDISON-WESLEY PUBLISHING COMPANY, INC.

Headquarters:
Reading, Massachusetts 01867

School Division Office:
3220 Porter Drive, Palo Alto, California 94304

Sales Office:
411 Elm Street, Dallas, Texas 75202

Sales Office:
10–15 Chitty Street, London W 1, England

Preface

It might seem that an appropriate time to write an elementary description of ideas in a scientific field is when that corner of knowledge has been well explored and fully illuminated. In the case of particle physics, we can at present only hope that we are *not* in a corner. As for illumination, there has been a great deal of it in the last ten years, showing us on every occasion problems that we had not recognized before. Nevertheless, a very substantial body of experimental facts and theory will probably remain unchanged by any future fashions of interpretation.

The current ferment of ideas concerning fundamental particles is caused by the intrinsic importance of the fundamental interactions, the new discoveries at the high energy machines made possible by new technology, and the large number of physicists attracted to such work. As is the nature of strong interactions, each of these factors is in turn created by the others. The excitement of the chase is apparent to anyone connected with physics—research workers, teachers, and students at all levels. There has even been competition between the popular press and scientific journals for scoops about new discoveries.

Under such circumstances, there is a justification for attempts to summarize the field sufficiently so that physics students at least can follow what is happening. At some early point in their career, physics students should hear the words and notions about particle physics so that they can listen with some understanding to research reports and share in the excitement. Graduate students with a background of quantum mechanics and the mathematics that goes with it can tackle current problems in particle physics with the same tools used by the people doing the research. For students without this background, understanding can come only in terms of word pictures and analogies. These can be very powerful, and indeed, many research workers make constant use of this type of understanding in planning and performing significant work. Probably because of the human need for the mental image type of perception, most successful theories can eventually be interpreted in terms of nonmathematical models, regardless of how abstract they are to begin with. There are obvious dangers in taking any model too seriously, including mathematical ones. In using analogies and word pictures in this book, I have tried to strike proper notes of caution.

This book is written for those who have studied physics for at least one year. Actually, specific facts from such a course and mathematics beyond algebra need not be known in order to follow any argument given here. The elusive quality known as technical and mathematical sophistication is necessary, however. During the last few years I have described particle physics in the terms used in this book to many audiencies composed of scientists and engineers from other fields, of college students, and of high school physics teachers and their bright students. Many such groups visit Brookhaven National Laboratory

12539

every year, and it was there that I first faced the reporter's problem of whether it is more important to tell the truth or to leave a truthful impression. Hopefully, I have so hedged the written word in this book that cases of outright falsehoods (as opposed to errors) are few. I would hope even more that the hedging has not obscured useful insight. It will be greatly appreciated if readers will draw to my attention examples of either type of sin.

Many of my colleagues at Brookhaven National Laboratory and State University of New York at Stony Brook have helped by discussing with me specific points made in the book. I am particularly grateful to Professor Peter Kahn of State University and Professor Arthur Rosenfeld of the University of California, who reviewed the whole text and made many useful suggestions.

Stony Brook, N.Y.   C.E.S.
November, 1964

Contents

Section 1. Building Blocks and Classification Schemes

PROLOGUE

Beyond our own swirling island of stars, billions of similar galaxies race toward the edges of the universe. Within the cells of our fingertips the molecules bind and unbind, and within realms a million times smaller than this, the particles of the atomic nuclei cling tightly together. Midway between the cosmos and the microworld, man tries to make sense of it all (Fig. 1).

The problem of understanding is not just one of relative size. The complexity of the materials in the world has always bewildered man. There are solids, liquids, gases, and that fourth state of matter that includes most of the universe—plasmas. There are the living and the inanimate. There are the plants and the animals. There are birds and fish, reptiles and mammals.

But of course, in describing the complexity we have already begun to simplify it. We classify the world. Wherever regularities or similarities can be observed, we establish categories. This part of existence goes in box A, that part in box B! It is the most primitive form of science we can use. These classification schemes can be silly or useful or dangerous; they can be the beginning of knowledge or the end of it.

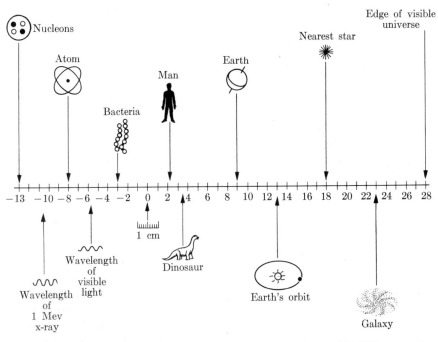

FIG. 1. Universe on log scale: 0 = 1 cm; 2 = 1 meter; 6 = 1,000,000 cm; −2 = .01 cm; etc.

This book describes some classification schemes which correlate facts about the building blocks of the universe. We should not underestimate the triumph that has been achieved with these schemes, but it would be deceptive to think that the structure of matter is now completely revealed. Classification schemes have sometimes frozen knowledge. There have been many attempts in the past to build a master scheme that would describe everything in the world. The idea is very old that there are building blocks from which everything else is constructed, depending only on the arrangement. Empedocles summarized one such system in Greece 2400 years ago. In Fig. 2 are shown the constituents of his universe—four elements and four essences.

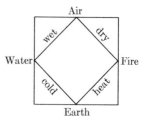

FIG. 2. The elements and essences of the Greek universe.

Poor naive Greeks, to think that they could encompass all the complexity of existence with such a simple scheme. At least such may be our first reaction to Empedocles' system. Upon reflection, however, we find that the Greek viewpoint is rather profound. This water that they spoke of is not the ordinary water that we use and drink; this was the Platonic ideal water. Ordinary water consists of the ideal water plus air and earth. If you don't believe it, add the essence of heat and watch the air come out, or apply cold and observe how earthlike it becomes. Strike a match and see how there is fire in ordinary earth, and as the flame is smothered, observe the air and earth in ordinary fire.

Yet this system led only to alchemy and the vain search for methods of turning one substance into another. There are many examples of such delusions in the history of science. Kepler tried to fit the planetary distances into a preconceived system based on musical harmonic relationships (so that the morning stars might sing together).

The greatest triumph for classification schemes came a little over one hundred years ago. Mendeléeff finally succeeded in a task that had been attempted by a whole generation of chemists before him. By this time there were many indications that matter was composed of tiny building blocks and that there were only a few types of these building blocks. It was also obvious that many of the recently isolated elements were chemically similar to each other. The problem was to systematize the enormous amount of information which had been obtained, some of it valid, and some quite misleading. Mendeléeff's chart of 1872 is shown in Fig. 3. The organization was based on chemical properties, not atomic weight. We know today that the system is really based on the atomic number; that is, the number of electrons in the atoms. The electronic arrangement determines the chemical behavior of the element. Yet, without knowing

Series	Group							
	I	II	III	IV	V	VI	VII	VIII
1	H							
2	Li	Be	B	C	N	O	F	
3	Na	Mg	Al	Si	P	S	Cl	
4	K	Ca		Ti	V	Cr	Mn	Fe Co Ni Cu
5	(Cu)	Zn			As	Se	Br	
6	Rb	Sr	Yt	Zr	Nb	Mo		Ru Rh Pd Ag
7	(Ag)	Cd	In	Sn	Sb	Te	I	
8	Cs	Ba	Di	Ce				
9								
10			Er	La	Ta	W		Os Ir Pt Au
11	(Au)	Hg	Tl	Pb	Bi			
12				Th		U		

FIG. 3. Mendeléeff's Periodic Table of 1872. The groups were based on chemical combining characteristics and not on atomic weight.

this information, Mendeléeff was able to predict the properties of unknown elements and to point out correctly errors in the existing data. It took another fifty years before the relationship between the periodic table and atomic structure was understood. Its regularities and successful predictions served as a great testing ground for all the atomic theories that were proposed, and when finally all the details were encompassed by our modern theory of the atom, there could be no doubt of its correctness.

There are two points to be noted here. Other people had also tried to organize the elements but they chose the wrong parameter. Obviously there are many attributes of each element. They could be arranged according to color, for example, but it would not be a very useful scheme. The problem, of course, is to know which of the parameters or attributes are the vital ones. (In the case of the particles, some of the attributes may be understood only in terms of the organizing scheme that makes use of them!) Secondly, in spite of the marvelous way in which the properties of the elements were predicted and arranged, there was no underlying theory as to why the regularities should appear. It was only the beginning of knowledge. Besides, there were too many types of building blocks. The Greeks had explained everything with only four. Our grandfathers needed ninety-two.

WHAT IS A FUNDAMENTAL PARTICLE?

There are some classification charts of the particles which we consider in this book. Now that a warning has been issued that classifications are not at all the same as basic theories, it might seem reasonable to proceed briskly with the business of explaining the arrangements and symbols. But the problem is not so simple. What, for instance, is a particle, and in what sense is it fundamental? Are these things real, and what about the crude question as to whether they are matter or energy? How do we see a proton or meson?

The names of some of the particles are familiar to everyone these days. By "particle" we mean things like protons, neutrons, and electrons. In fact, those three are the building blocks of the atoms, and thus of all the elements. Whether or not they are fundamental or elementary is another question. The words imply that such a particle is not composed of anything more fundamental, and so presumably does not have internal structure. Thus we rule out the atoms themselves, since the protons, neutrons, and electrons within them seem to be clearly differentiated. Note, however, that no particular experiment demands that the electron lead an independent existence *in* the atom. It is our successful *model* of the atom which views the electron as maintaining its identity in the system. When energy is applied to matter in the proper way, electrons are emitted from all substances. For that matter, so is light, and yet we do not think of light as being an independent constituent of atoms. To press the point further, in beta decay of radioactive materials, electrons are shot out from the atomic *nucleus*. In this case, as we shall see, our model insists that the electrons were not in the nuclei to begin with but were created on the spur of the moment. We view this interpretation as the "truth," simply because the model is so successful in correlating a vast number of experimental facts.

From an experimental point of view, an excited hydrogen atom is quite a different particle from one in the ground state. Nevertheless, we know the process by which it changes from one situation to another, and can describe the operation in terms of subunits which need not change their characteristics during the process. Therefore, we usually think of the hydrogen atom as being just one particular system which can exist in different states or arrangements. By using these same standards, most of the particles we shall investigate cannot be considered fundamental. Within several family groupings, they change into each other with ease. Indeed, we shall see that even during their transient existence before decay, they must be considered to be partially themselves and partially other systems with which they are related. The heavier particles (including the proton and neutron) may not even have a core identity of their own; perhaps each exists only because of, and in terms of, its interactions with all the others.

Although it is convenient to think of protons and neutrons as the subunits of atomic nuclei, they can hardly be considered to be fundamental and certainly not elementary. The neutron, for instance, is radioactive. When free of an atomic nucleus, it decays into a proton, electron, and neutrino, although no theory views it as composed of those particles. Since 1958 it has been clear that both proton and neutron have an internal structure which can be probed with high-energy particles. The total charge of the neutron adds to zero, but the distribution of charge in the spinning system makes it act like a magnet. For our present purposes, we should abandon any attempt to define what we mean by "fundamental." The problem will face us once again in the final chapter.

There is a feeling in some quarters that an object is in some way not quite real if it cannot be seen. True enough, the particles are too small to be seen in the usual sense by means of visible light, but of course we see them as clearly as we see anything else in this world. Look at a friend. Light strikes his features, scatters into your eye and triggers an electrochemical response in some nerves. Many such signals are relayed to a computing center in your brain where they are in some way matched to a recognition pattern stored there. You have "seen" your friend. A cloud chamber expands, creating a region of supersaturated air. The vapor trail that occurs scatters light into your eyes. The signals match the recognition pattern that you have established for a particular kind of particle. You have "seen" a proton. If you protest that there is one extra step involved, that actually you have only seen the trail of damaged atoms left by the proton, then consider whether or not you have really seen your friend, or only some outward appearance. Give your friend the benefit of the doubt and admit that there may be more to him than can be caught by scattered light. Indeed, the proton is much simpler, and therefore we can see it far more completely than we ever can see a human. It has only a few attributes, all measurable, and they remain stable.

But are the particles real, even if they do trigger responses from instruments? With solid machinery that we can put our hands on, we create a certain experimental setup. Every few seconds a meter needle jumps and a light glows. We use a code term to describe the action: a "proton" passed through the instrument. You dial a phone number and through the agency of an enormously complex system, a pattern of sound waves is emitted from a metal diaphragm and disturbs a membrane in your ear. Your friend has answered the phone. Is he "real" or just a code word to simplify your explanation of the affair?

Section 2.   Bohr Atom

We shall still be devious in our attack on the microworld and describe first a model of the atom which will seem comfortably familiar to most people. Note that we study a model, not to avoid the truth, but to approach it. Do we know anything of our world except in terms of models and analogies?

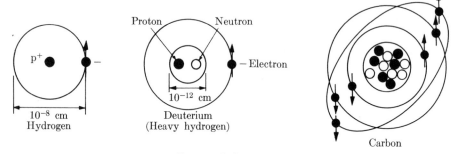

FIG. 4. Bohr atoms.

Model 1, the Bohr atom, out of style now these 35 years (Fig. 4). The atom has a solar-system construction with a small positive nucleus containing most of the atomic mass. The nucleus controls the orbital motions of negative electrons. These electrons are constrained to follow specific orbits which can exist only at a few discrete (separate, individually distinct) distances from the nucleus. Therefore the electric potential energy of the electrons trapped in these special orbits or "shells" must also have discrete values.

The useful features which remain valid are considered in the following sections.

SIZE—MASS

Each atom, or smallest unit of an element, is an electrically neutral object about 10^{-8} centimeter in diameter. (From hydrogen to uranium the size never varies by more than a factor of 2.) If we consider this number as a fraction of which the denominator represents the number of atoms, side by side, which can be contained in one centimeter of length, we observe that about 100 million atoms are required to cover one centimeter of length. In a centimeter cube, therefore, the number of atoms is $(10^8)^3 = 10^{24}$. (Because of the factor of 2 in linear size, the number in a centimeter cube may be only 10^{23}.) The reader who remembers his chemistry will see that we have arrived at Avogadro's number, or close to it. This number, sometimes called the "mole," equals 6×10^{23}. A mole of atoms has a mass in grams equal to the number called the atomic weight. A mole of hydrogen atoms has a mass of 1 gm, a mole of deuterium atoms has a mass of 2 gm, a mole of uranium atoms has a mass of about 238 gm. Since most of the mass of the atom resides in the nucleus, and since

$\sim 10^{24}$ hydrogen atoms weigh 1 gm, then each atom and hence each proton must weigh 10^{-24} gm. The neutron must weigh about the same, at least while it is in the nucleus. A finer comparison will be made later.

VALENCE ELECTRONS

The chemical nature of the atom is mostly determined by the arrangement of electrons in orbit which in turn is determined by the number of protons in the nucleus. Most of the electrons seem to exist in definite regions, or shells, or orbits with only the outermost taking part in chemical combinations.

ISOTOPES

There can exist variations of atoms of a particular element. These isotopes all have the same number of protons and electrons (and hence the same chemical properties), but the nucleus may contain varying numbers of neutrons. Hydrogen, for example has three isotopes, which in this special case have been given special names:

Nucleus consists of:

Hydrogen	1 proton	$_1\text{H}^1$
Deuterium	1 proton, 1 neutron	$_1\text{D}^2$
Tritium	1 proton, 2 neutrons	$_1\text{T}^3$

PERIODIC TABLE

The arrangement of electrons in the orbits determines the nature of the periodic table. The negative electrons are pulled toward the positive nucleus but must take up specific positions to satisfy laws which we shall detail later. The most important of these is that no two electrons in the same atom can have

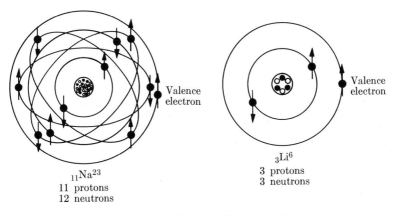

$_{11}\text{Na}^{23}$
11 protons
12 neutrons

Valence electron

$_3\text{Li}^6$
3 protons
3 neutrons

Valence electron

FIG. 5. Periodicity of electron shells.

exactly the same values for their measurable characteristics. As the allowable positions of electrical potential become filled, any additional electrons must occupy unfilled orbits at greater distances from the nucleus. The inner allowed regions, or shells, are closed. The periodicity in Mendeléeff's table arises because an atom with one electron outside its first closed shell (lithium) acts chemically like the much heavier atom (sodium) with one electron outside its second closed shell (Fig. 5).

BINDING ENERGY

The negative electrons are trapped by the positive charge of the nucleus in almost exactly the same way that objects are trapped on the earth by gravitation. To escape from this potential well (Fig. 6), a certain minimum energy is needed, equal to $\frac{1}{2}mv_e^2$, where v_e is the escape velocity. The amount of this energy for the outermost electrons in atoms is just the magnitude of energy involved in chemical interactions. Every time there is one chemical transformation in a flashlight battery, one electron is shoved up an electric potential hill of $1\frac{1}{2}$ volts. The amount of energy involved equals the charge times the voltage. A convenient unit of energy is *electron volt*, one electron charge raised one volt in potential. Since most chemical transformations involve about this much energy transfer (per molecule), it appears to be a basic energy unit for the microworld. Since we humans are usually concerned with the energy transfer of many grams of material, the electron volt is much smaller than our standard energy units of foot-pounds or kilowatt-hours or watt-seconds (the joule).

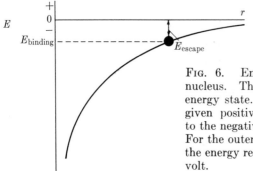

FIG. 6.   Energy graph of electron in field of nucleus. The electrons are bound in a negative energy state. For them to escape, they must be given positive kinetic energy, $E = \frac{1}{2}mv^2$, equal to the negative energy by which they are trapped. For the outermost electrons in atoms or molecules, the energy required is of the order of one electron volt.

If a flashlight battery produces one ampere for one second, the energy produced is $1\frac{1}{2}$ watt-sec. During this time 6×10^{18} electrons have been sent through the battery as the result of 6×10^{18} molecular recombinations. Since each cubic centimeter of the battery material has about 10^{24} molecules in it, many more chemical reactions are still available. The watt-second or joule of energy, is equal to 6×10^{18} electron volts. The joule is useful in the macroworld; the electron volt is appropriate in the world of particles. The abbreviation for electron volt is *ev*; for million (10^6) electron volts, *Mev*; for billion (10^9) electron volts, *Bev* (or in Europe, *Gev*).

A formal definition of these energy terms is implied by the names of two of them. For instance, a foot-pound is the amount of work done by exerting a force of one pound through a distance of one foot. An electron volt is the amount of work done in lifting one electron through a potential difference of one volt. As we shall see, electric charge is quantized; that is, it can exist only in multiples of a basic unit. The charge of the electron is just one such basic unit and is negative. The energy unit might have been called "charge volt," or "proton volt."

We shall use the electron volt as the unit of energy throughout the book even when talking about the energy of protons and neutrons. After all, you use a yardstick even when you are not measuring your back yard.

NUCLEUS

The nucleus, although containing most of the mass of the atom, occupies an infinitesimal fraction of the volume. In diameter it is smaller by a factor of 10^4 to 10^5. If the nucleus of hydrogen (the proton) were as large as a child's marble, the electron would usually be found at a distance of one-eighth of a mile.

The size of the nucleus increases steadily with the number of nucleons (protons and neutrons) in it, and in just the manner we would expect if the nucleus were hard spheres packed together (Fig. 7). The radius should be proportional to the cube root of the volume, which in turn will be roughly proportional to the number of nucleons. Indeed, the radius of most nuclei is accurately described by the formula: $r = r_0 A^{1/3}$ where r_0 is about the radius of a proton or neutron, 1.3×10^{-13} cm, and A is the number of nucleons, protons plus neutrons. There are some interesting exceptions to this rule for the very light nuclei.

Volume $\propto A$

$r \propto A^{1/3}$

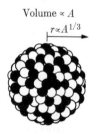

FIG. 7. Hard sphere model of nucleus. The nuclear radii are proportional to the 1/3 power of the number of nucleons (A) in them.

Our world, according to this model, is a simple place indeed. The ninety-two elements and all their isotopes are just varying configurations of three fundamental particles: proton, neutron, and electron. Nature is not going to yield that easily, however. Even by the time the neutron was discovered in 1932, other particles were being suggested by certain experiments and theories. Before complicating the world again, we shall first describe some features of the most familiar particle, the electron. Our attempt will be to define the properties of this well-known particle in terms of the experimental effects that can be observed. Most of the attributes of the electron have their counterparts for other particles. An understanding of its behavior will simplify the rest of the story. In the process, we shall see why the old Bohr atom with definite electron orbits is an unsatisfactory model for many phenomena.

Section 3.   The Electron, a Familiar Particle

The first particle to be actually identified as such was the electron. In 1897, J. J. Thomson measured the charge to mass ratio (e/m) of the particles coming from a negative terminal inside a vacuum system. The existence of "cathode rays" had been known for some years and it had been shown that they carried negative charge. It was conceivable, however, that the rays were simply a stream of electric current. Thomson's experiment of deflecting the path of the rays with electric and magnetic fields was most easily explained in terms of the motion of individual particles.

PRODUCTION

The electron is the easiest particle to isolate. Experimenters seventy years ago were intrigued with the way electrons seemed to leap out of any substance with only the mildest encouragement. Certain minimum conditions are necessary, of course. Electrical instruments are needed to detect most of the effects, and these effects mostly take place in high vacuum. To drive an electron out of a material, it is necessary to give it sufficient energy to escape from its atomic or molecular bonds. With some metals this can be done by heating the whole system and boiling off the electrons. They can also be knocked out by light, as in the photoelectric effect (Fig. 8). As we saw earlier, the amount of extra escape energy needed is a few electron volts. Ordinary blue light can provide about 3 ev per encounter, which is sufficient for electron emission from the alkali metals. Ultraviolet, which can deliver energy of 6 to 10 ev to each electron, could knock electrons out of chicken fat, were that desirable (and assuming that the ultraviolet could get through the air without being absorbed by knocking electrons out of the air molecules).

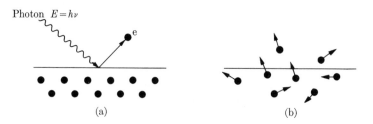

(a)   (b)

Fig. 8.   (a) Photoelectric emission: $h\nu = E_{escape} + \frac{1}{2}mv^2$. (b) Thermal emission: $E_{thermal} = E_{escape} + \frac{1}{2}mv^2$.

The average energy of a molecule at room temperature is about $\frac{1}{25}$ ev. A tungsten filament in a vacuum tube may be heated to 3000° kelvin, ten times as hot as the 300°K room temperature. An energy of only 0.4 ev would not be enough to cause an electron to be emitted from tungsten, but that is only the average energy. The high-energy end of the distribution (Fig. 9), can give sufficiently energetic kicks to electrons frequently enough to make the white-hot filament a very generous electron emitter.

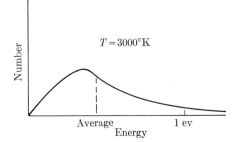

Fig. 9. Thermal distribution of energy for gas molecules. The electrons in a conductor do not behave completely like molecules in a gas, but their average thermal energy is similarly much lower than the high energies possessed by some of them.

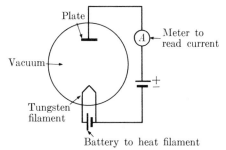

Fig. 10. Simple diode to demonstrate negative current emission.

CHARGE

The diagram of the diode in Fig. 10 shows a way to demonstrate that something negative is coming from the filament to the receiving plate. In spite of the success of Thompson's particle model, however, it is still conceivable that this negative charge is flowing as some kind of fluid instead of traveling in individual packages. A single electron would not make even the most sensitive electrical detector in this circuit respond with a signal greater than the natural fluctuations of the instrument. The individual charge was first measured accurately by Millikan in 1903. With a microscope he observed tiny oil spray droplets rising and falling between the plates of an electrical condenser (Fig. 11). They fall, because of their weight, of course, but they travel at different speeds, both up and down, because one or more electric charges become attached to the droplet. Because of air friction and the small droplet size, terminal velocity is produced. Under these circumstances the net force is proportional to the speed

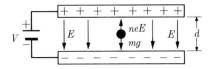

Fig. 11. Millikan determination of discrete electric charge. Electric field strength is $E = V/d$; net force is $mg - neE \propto v$; mg is weight of oil drop; n is number of discrete charges on drop; e is value of discrete charge.

(instead of acceleration). For a given droplet, several different velocities are possible. If the velocity changed steadily, we would have to assume that electric charge was leaking on or off in a continuous fashion, but instead only certain discrete velocities appear for each droplet. Since terminal velocity is proportional to the force, the force must be exerted in certain discrete amounts only. But this electrical force is equal to the net electric charge on the droplet times the electric field in the condenser. The field remains constant, and therefore the electric charge must exist only in certain discrete amounts. The amount of electric charge that can cling to a droplet is quantized (exists in multiples of unit quantities), and Millikan's experiment yielded a quantitative value for the magnitude of charge. It is negative and equal to 1.6×10^{-19} coulomb (coul), the unit of charge used in electrical work. A coulomb is the amount of charge transferred by a current of one ampere flowing for one second. In terms of the fundamental electron charge, therefore, one ampere is the flow of

$$\frac{1}{1.6 \times 10^{-19}} = 6 \times 10^{18}$$

electrons passing a given point each second.

MASS

The most obvious attribute of the electron is its charge. The next question is, does it have any mass? To measure the mass of a baseball, we have two methods. First, we can measure the weight or, in other words, the attractive force between baseball and earth. Because the weight is proportional to the mass, $F = G(mM/r^2)$, we can compare the weights (and so the masses) of baseball and standard mass on a balance. The second method depends on the inertial properties of mass, its reluctance to have its state of motion changed. When a force is applied to an object, the object accelerates: $F \propto a$. The constant of proportionality is called mass: $F = ma$. The mass of the baseball could be found by applying a known force to it and measuring the acceleration produced.

The first method is completely impractical for finding the mass of the electron. No experiment has been performed where the gravitational effect on the electron could be observed. The force—the weight—is just too small. But because the electron has charge, electromagnetic forces can be exerted on it with much larger effects than the gravitational. The bubble chamber tracks of Plate I* clearly show the result of electron acceleration. The electron velocity was continually being changed by a force perpendicular to the path. Such a perpendicular or centripetal force does not change the speed or energy of the electron but does make it move in a circular path. In the bubble chamber picture, the tracks are spirals because the electrons were constantly losing energy in their passage through the gas. The perpendicular force caused by the movement of the electron in a magnetic field is Bev, where B is the strength of the magnetic field, e is the electron charge, and v is its velocity. A centripetal acceleration

---

* The plates appear following p. 57.

must thus be produced with magnitude v^2/r, where r is the radius of the circular path. Since $F = ma$, it follows that

$$Bev = m\frac{v^2}{r}.$$

Solving for m, we have

$$m_{\text{electron}} = \frac{Ber}{v}.$$

If the velocity of the electron is known, its mass can be determined. There are many ways to combine magnetic and electric forces acting on electrons or other particles so that the mass can be determined. For the electron, the value turns out to be 9×10^{-31} kg.

There is yet another way of measuring the mass of the electron, depending on an effect which appears quite different from the inertial ones, although really not independent of inertia. Instead of forcing an existing electron to change its motion, create a new electron! This takes energy, of course, in an amount equal to mc^2, where c is the velocity of light and m is the created mass. The bubble chamber picture of Plate I shows such an event. A photon, or in other words a bundle of electromagnetic energy, came from the left and in the vicinity of a particular atom, turned all its energy into the mass and kinetic energy of two electrons. In the magnetic field the two electrons circled in opposite senses; one was negative, our standard electron, and one was positive, the so-called positron. If only one electron were created, a unit of electric charge would have come from nowhere. This never happens; the total charge remains constant. There was none to begin with and the net amount ($+$ plus $-$) afterward is also zero. It takes an x-ray of at least 1 Mev to produce such a pair creation. Each electron uses half of this for its mass. If any is left over, the electrons can share it to provide forward motion. So in this other way of measuring the mass of an electron we find that the mass is 0.51 Mev. The arithmetic of course works out:

$$mc^2 = 9 \times 10^{-31} \text{ kg} \times (3 \times 10^8 \text{ m/sec})^2$$
$$= 81 \times 10^{-15} \text{ joules (watt-sec)}.$$

Since

$$1.6 \times 10^{-19} \text{ joules} = 1 \text{ ev},$$
$$mc^2 = 0.51 \times 10^6 \text{ ev} \approx \tfrac{1}{2} \text{ Mev}.$$

SPIN

The electron has yet another attribute that is vital to its interactions. Besides having mass and electric charge, it acts as if it were spinning on its own axis. Such a spin can make itself known through three main effects.

1. Magnetic moment. (a) First of all, a spinning electric charge becomes a small magnet. In a uniform magnetic field the electrons should align themselves like compass needles all pointing together (Fig. 12). If for any reason some of

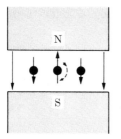

Fig. 12.   Alignment of magnets in a magnetic field.

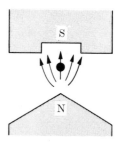

Fig. 13. A magnetic dipole experiences a translational force in an inhomogeneous magnetic field. The force is stronger on the bottom than on the top of the dipole.

them are forced out of alignment, they will be in a different energy state from the stable ones. When they swing back into line, their energy will be released in some form, since energy had to be provided to get them out of line in the first place. Furthermore in a nonuniform magnetic field, the electron magnets should not only rotate but should move toward or away from the region of strong field. These effects can be detected with a bit of trickery.

Figure 13 shows magnet pole pieces that provide a very nonuniform magnetic field. As you can see, a magnet with its north end up will move down in the diagram; the force down on the south end is greater than the force up on the north. If a beam of electrons is shot through such a magnetic field, we might expect the emerging beam to spread out in a vertical line. The deviation of each electron would depend on how its spin was oriented when it entered. We assume that the spin of each would not flip into line while going through the magnet, but instead would precess like a top, still maintaining its original angle to the vertical. But, of course, the experiment cannot be done quite so simply. Not only would the electrons spread out slightly vertically, but because they are charged particles moving in a magnetic field they would be forced in a direction perpendicular to their velocity and to the magnetic field. Instead of using bare charged electrons, the actual experiment is done by having the electrons ride along on an atom. Silver was used by Stern and Gerlach in 1924. Silver has just one valence electron, existing in a state such that the only angular momentum or spin must be that associated with the electron itself. All the other electrons in the closed shells produce effects that cancel. The whole atom is electrically neutral so that it will not be influenced by a magnetic field unless the atom is also behaving like a small magnet, in which case it will be deviated up or down. Figure 14 shows the experimental method and results. Some atoms were indeed forced up and others down, but only into two groups! Apparently the electron spins were either in line with the field or 180° out of line. The effect is quantized. If the whole system were rotated on its axis 90°, we would find that the deviations were then horizontal, but still divided into two definite groups with nothing in between. Thus the directional deviation is not a function of the way the atomic beam was produced. The silver atoms are boiled out of the oven with completely random orientation. We are forced by this phenomenon (and many others) to conclude that the electron spin can exist only in line or out of line with the magnetic field with which we detect it. One is tempted to insist that in the original beam the spins must have had any orientation and somehow arranged themselves in this peculiar way just when they entered the magnetic field. Perhaps so, but of course that is metaphysics and meaningless. If an effect can never be detected, directly or indirectly, then it is rather useless to ponder it. In any experimental arrangement where electron spin is determined, some standard direction or axis is established. The electrons are always found to be lined up either in that particular direction or opposite to it, but never in between.

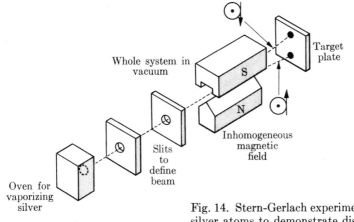

Fig. 14. Stern-Gerlach experiment using neutral silver atoms to demonstrate discrete alignment of magnetic moments.

The convenient unit of angular momentum for particles is Planck's constant (divided by 2π). In the literature of physics this is written as the symbol $\hbar = h/2\pi$. It has the value of 1×10^{-34} joule-sec and, of course, the proper dimensions to be angular momentum (Mass · Length^2/Time).

It is rather startling that there is a natural unit of angular momentum in this world. We know of very few other quantities which have basic units which exist naturally. There are none for mass, length, or time—so far as we know. Electrical charge has a natural unit, and now we find one for angular momentum. In terms of this unit, the electron has spin $\frac{1}{2}$. As we shall see, this is a very significant value. Particles cannot have just any value of spin, but only certain ones. Like electric charge, spin is quantized and can exist in multiples of $\frac{1}{2}\hbar$, but never with values in between, such as $0.65\hbar$. Furthermore, the measured values for a given system, corresponding to the different directions of the spin, must always be different from each other by one whole unit, $\hbar$. Therefore the valence electron of silver is found in only two orientations, with the direction-giving field $(+\frac{1}{2})$ or against $(-\frac{1}{2})$.

(b) The magnetic-moment effect of the electron spin can also be determined in *uniform* magnetic fields. For this it is necessary to use atoms or molecules with unpaired electrons; the goal is to deal with electrons relatively free and yet bound sufficiently so that a large number can be held in one place. The conduction electrons in a metal are plentiful enough, but they are by no means independent agents. A conduction electron could not orient itself in a magnetic field without interacting with all the others. Most of the electrons in material are paired off with electrons of opposite spin existing in the same energy level. There are, however, a number of substances containing unpaired electrons which do not have to interact with the neighboring atoms to form molecular bonds.

If one of these substances is placed in a magnetic field, the electron spins will point either with or against the field. It would seem at first that all of them would flip around so as to align themselves and thus be in the lowest possible energy state. But actually, energy is being fed into the electron spin system by the random heat motion of the molecules. It is as though a group of compass needles were trying to line up in a magnetic field but were constantly being jiggled into random directions.

The amount of energy that it takes to flip one electron in a particular magnetic field is a very definite amount:

$$2\mu_e B \approx 2 \times 10^{-27} B_{\text{gauss}} \text{ joules} \approx 10^{-8} B_{\text{gauss}} \text{ ev} = 10^{-5} \text{ ev} \quad \text{for 1000 gauss,}$$

where μ_e is the magnetic moment of the electron. (Magnetic moment is the measure of strength of a magnetic dipole, and is best defined and measured in terms of this equation.) It would take a chunk of electromagnetic energy of just this amount to flip the electron, and of course, if the electron flips back, a photon of that energy is emitted. Photon energy is directly related to frequency. Thus,

$$E = h\nu,$$

where h is Planck's constant and ν is frequency in cycles per second. In this particular example, a magnetic field of 1000 gauss* would require photons or radio signals with a frequency of about 3000 megacycles. Normally, such a signal is not heard from the sample. As many electrons are flipping one way as the other to maintain the particular balance determined by the temperature. If, however, a radio coil is placed around the sample, as shown in Fig. 15, and the frequency is gradually raised, in one particular narrow frequency range the coil will appear to absorb extra energy from the transmitter. This energy has produced the flipping of many electrons out of the magnetic field direction. How long it takes for them to jiggle back depends on the temperature and how easily the substance transmits its thermal agitation to the electrons.

Figure 15 shows a typical plot obtained in such an experiment. In this case the frequency remained constant and the magnetic field was changed.

---

* The horizontal component of the field of the earth is $\approx \frac{1}{5}$ gauss at the surface in New York City.

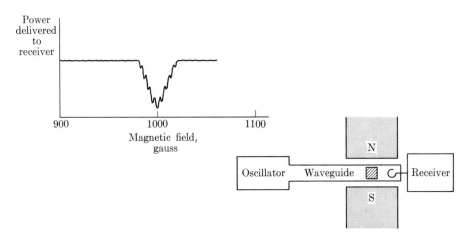

Fig. 15. Absorption of radar frequency energy due to electron magnetic resonance. The various maxima correspond to various local fields in which the electrons may exist in the structure.

(c) The different energy states of the electron as it assumes the two orientations (either in or out of the magnetic field) give rise to spectroscopic effects that were observed over a hundred years ago. However, we had to wait until 1924 for the interpretation, which was made by Goudsmit and Uhlenbeck. Strong magnetic fields of the order of 10^5 gauss can exist naturally inside atoms. The electronic circulation (in the older picture, the orbital motion of electrons) produces fields which interact with the magnetic effects of the intrinsic spin of each electron. Since light is produced by the jump of an outside electron into a vacant position that has been momentarily created in the orbits, the energy of the light pulse will be equal to the difference in energy levels of the jumping electron.

Each energy level really has two possible values, corresponding to the two orientations the electron can assume with respect to the local fields. As can be seen in Fig. 16 this will give fine structure to every type of transition. Instead of producing a photon of light with one particular energy, and so a particular wavelength, each transition produces a double or triple wavelength in the spectrum.

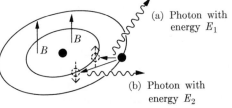

(a) Photon with energy E_1

(b) Photon with energy E_2

Fig. 16. Electron spin splitting of spectral lines. $E_1 > E_2$ since in (b) part of the energy is still retained by the electron in being oriented against the magnetic field.

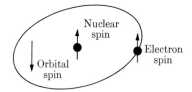

Vector Combination of Angular Momenta

Single electron in p-orbit of angular momentum $1\hbar$

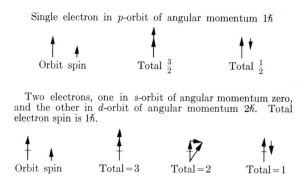

Fig. 17.   Angular momentum vectors in an atom.

2. Angular momentum, a second effect of spin.   Electron spin must also be taken into account in spectroscopy and in particle decays where electrons are emitted, simply because of the fact that spin means angular momentum and that is one of the few things in this world that are rigorously conserved. (A more complete discussion of angular momentum is given in Section 6.) If an atomic system emits a photon of light, the photon carries off one whole unit of angular momentum. (The fact that photons possess angular momentum has been experimentally demonstrated.) The remaining system must then be one unit different from what it was to begin with. If the photon carries off clockwise angular momentum, the remaining system must recoil counterclockwise. Within the system various parts are producing angular momentum, some associated with certain electron configurations (as though the electrons were actually orbiting around the nucleus, Fig. 17). Also, of course, we must take into account the spin, or intrinsic angular momentum, of each of the electrons. The nucleus has a spin, too. All of these must be added together, but the addition is vectorial; that is, many cancel. The spectral lines can be understood only when the description of total angular momentum includes the spins.

In particle decays, the same conservation principle must be satisfied. When a radioactive nucleus decays to emit an electron, a β-ray, there is an apparent breakdown of this rule. The parent nucleus recoils but it can do so with no change in its own spin. Yet the electron goes tearing off, spinning as it goes. It is as surprising as if a person on a friction-free table were able to get a bicycle wheel spinning without recoiling in the opposite sense himself. The very same

problem arises when the muon (one of the main
parts of cosmic rays at sea level) decays. A
single electron comes spinning out.
There is a way out, of course. In all such
cases, at least one other particle, the neutrino,
ν, is also emitted (Fig. 18). It has no electric
charge and so is not easily detected, but it does
have spin. The man on the friction-free table
would have no trouble getting two bicycle
wheels spinning, so long as one went clockwise and the other counterclockwise. The
neutrino and its problems will be dealt with
later after the full roll of the particles has
been called.

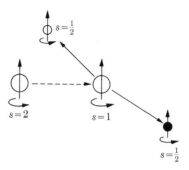

Fig. 18.   Nucleus with spin $2\hbar$
decays to nucleus with spin $1\hbar$,
plus electron and neutrino with
spin $\frac{1}{2}\hbar$ each.

3. The exclusion law, the third role of spin. The electron has intrinsic angular momentum, and so it acts like a magnet, but its spin of $\frac{1}{2}\hbar$ has an even more
profound effect. All particles with half odd-integral spin ($\frac{1}{2}, \frac{3}{2}, \frac{5}{2}, \ldots$), and this
includes protons and neutrons as well as electrons, must obey a special exclusion
law. The great physicist, Pauli, first framed this principle in 1925. Two other
great names in physics are associated with the particular rules resulting from
Pauli's principle, Fermi and Dirac. In scientific literature, particles with spin
$\frac{1}{2}\hbar, \frac{3}{2}\hbar$, etc., are referred to as "fermions." No two fermions can possess identical
properties while inhabiting the same region. It is this saturation restriction
that is responsible for the particular arrangement of electrons in the atoms and
so determines the nature of the periodic table (Fig. 19).

Hydrogen has one electron existing in a region close to the proton nucleus.
Helium has two electrons in the same region with all the same properties except
that the spins of the two electrons are in opposite directions. Lithium has three
electrons but only two can exist in the lowest allowed energy region. The third
electron in this region could have its spin aligned in only one of two ways, and
in either case, this would duplicate all of the properties of an electron already
there. If there were two kinds of electrons, red and blue, or if the electron had
some other kind of variable property, lopsidedness(?), then more than two could
fit into the same energy region. But only two do so. Thus it must be that the
electron has a limited number of attributes, and with spin we have exhausted
the list. The third electron of lithium must exist in a higher energy level, farther
from the nucleus. The fourth electron of beryllium can, with opposing spin,
associate with number three. The fifth electron of boron is almost in the same
second energy shell, but not quite because it can have one unit of angular
momentum (besides its intrinsic spin). This changes the energy slightly and
thus makes it distinguishable from electron number four. There can be three
directions of angular momentum of magnitude one. In any experimental situation which sets up a preferred direction (e.g. a magnetic field), the axis of the
system can either point with the field, against it, or perpendicular to it. Note the

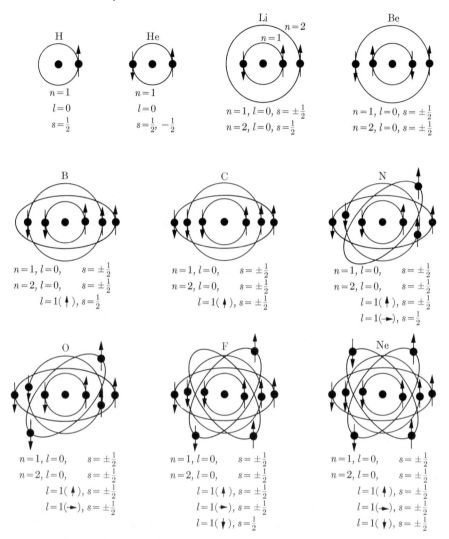

Fig. 19. Pauli exclusion principle and periodicity of Bohr orbit occupation.

difference between this situation and that for spin of $\frac{1}{2}\hbar$, which is quantized with only two possibilities.

The second energy level of an atom's electron system thus has four possible configurations: orbital angular momentum zero, and three orientations of orbital angular momentum one. Each of these can hold two electrons, spin "up" and "down." Altogether, eight electrons can fit into the second shell. Each of the electrons has properties that are experimentally distinguishable from those of the others. Even without an external field, the internal magnetic fields in an atom cause each of the eight electrons to have slightly different energies. These differences are represented in spectra by photons of slightly different wavelengths, producing "fine structure" or "splitting" of the spectral lines.

SIZE OF THE ELECTRON.   THE WAVE-PARTICLE PROBLEM

So far we have assigned only three attributes to the familiar electron: mass, charge, and spin. If we were describing a marble, we would already have inquired concerning its "looks": color, size, etc. (Actually, we have been describing the "looks" of the electron; that is, we have described the experimental responses to probes which can detect electrons.) Of course, the electron has no color simply because the shortest wavelength of visible light (4×10^{-7} meter for blue) is certainly larger than the size of an electron. One cannot determine the structure of an object with a probe larger than the object. There is a special problem concerned with the definition of particle size. In some cases the problem is as simple as the one we would face in measuring the "size" of a small bar magnet. With a meter stick, and using light and our eyes, we would get one result. Using a magnetic probe, we would apparently have a larger object with rather fuzzy edges. If a particle is responsive to several forces, it is possible that its boundaries may be different for each one.

But there is another size problem more subtle than this. Under certain conditions the behavior of electrons must be described in terms of the behavior of waves. The wavelength is related to the momentum by the following formula: $\lambda = h/p$. Here λ is the wavelength in meters, h is the ubiquitous Planck's constant, and p is the standard symbol used in the literature to represent momentum. At low velocities, $p = m_0 v$ (rest mass times velocity), the usual definition. At velocities close to the speed of light, the momentum is a more complicated function,

$$ p = \frac{m_0 v}{\sqrt{1 - (v^2/c^2)}}, $$

and experimentally assumes a more important role than either the mass or velocity separately.

Observe now how the size of the electron changes. Surely it is as large as one wavelength and presumably its influence would extend over several wavelengths. For an electron accelerated through 10 volts, perhaps in a radio tube, the velocity is $\approx 1.6 \times 10^6$ m/sec. Then

$$ \lambda = \frac{6.6 \times 10^{-34} \text{ joule-sec}}{9 \times 10^{-31} \text{ kg} \times 1.6 \times 10^6 \text{ m/sec}} \approx 5 \times 10^{-10} \text{ meter}. $$

(The outer electrons in atoms have momentum about equal to that indicated in the equation. Their wavelengths, therefore, are about the size which is indicated by the equation.) Since this wavelength is larger than the size of an atom, the point is emphasized that an electron cannot really be considered to be orbiting about a nucleus. In this sense, the electron is as large as the atom, and indeed there is no other sense. By any experiment that can be performed, the atomic electrons are found to exist over regions comparable in size to the whole atom. It is meaningless to ask how large the electrons are or where they are going during the time when we do not measure them.

There is, of course, good experimental evidence for the wave *behavior* of electrons. For our present arguments, we deliberately avoid the use of the words "wave nature." The similar wave behavior of light is most clearly seen in interference or diffraction patterns. Plate II shows a diffraction pattern produced by a beam of electrons passing through a hole produced by the spacing of atoms in a crystal. The pattern is very similar to that produced by light passing through a small hole. The spacing of the rings depends in both cases on the ratio of wavelengths to hole diameter. With red light the rings are spaced farther apart than with blue light. With slow electrons the spacing is larger than with fast electrons. The analysis of the optical phenomenon is in terms of waves originating in different regions of the hole, traveling different distances to the screen, and interfering with each other there, sometimes canceling and sometimes reinforcing. The ring geometry arises solely because with a round hole there must be circular symmetry. Since exactly the same phenomenon is observed with electrons, we use the same language and the mathematics of wave motion to describe the situation. We need not concern ourselves as to whether or not an electron *is* a wave. It *is* an electron. In situations where it interacts with objects larger than the wavelength given by $\lambda = h/p$, it acts like a hard spinning sphere. When the interaction is with objects comparable in size to λ, or smaller, the effect has to be described in terms of the interactions of waves. There is a similar situation with sound. The behavior of high-frequency sound in a room is very much like that of "rays" bouncing about. The low-frequency sounds, however, curl around corners like waves. In mathematical descriptions of processes, this dual state of affairs is very common. We may have a particular formula or equation which is complicated and difficult to compute or solve, but which is completely accurate at all times. This is exactly the case for our description of photons and any electromagnetic interactions. To obtain a solution for a particular case, the usual technique is to make certain approximations. An exact solution to most physical problems is never possible, and part of the skill of the mathematician or scientist lies in choosing the right approximation, and knowing to what accuracy the solution should be carried.

For instance, consider the equation describing the fall of an object through air. Gravitational force acts downward; air resistance (proportional to the square of the velocity) opposes the motion with a force directed up. The net force produces acceleration:

$$mg(\downarrow) - kv^2(\uparrow) = ma.$$

In differential form:

$$mg - k\left(\frac{dy}{dt}\right)^2 = m\frac{d^2y}{dt^2}.$$

This differential equation can be solved by separation of variables. In either of two limits, however, the solution is elementary. If the object is streamlined so that k is small or dy/dt is small because the object has just started to drop, we have the approximation of a freely falling object in vacuum.

Approximation 1: $\Delta y = \frac{1}{2}gt^2$ ($v_0 = 0$).

If, at the other extreme, the terminal velocity has been reached, there is no net force and the velocity is constant.

Approximation 2: $\Delta y = v_{\text{terminal}} t$ $(v_0 = 0)$.

Here we have two different solutions to the same equation! Naturally there is no paradox, because we know that these solutions are approximations valid under particular—and different—circumstances.

The so-called paradox of wave-particle duality is not much more complicated than this. There are, in quantum electrodynamics, complete equations describing electromagnetic interactions. Which approximation, which mental model we choose, depends on the physical situation. When particles are interacting with low energy, the mathematical description is usually best approximated with equations which are something like the wave equations of classical mechanics. Thus we speak of quantum mechanics as "wave mechanics." On the other hand, the motion of a high-energy particle can sometimes be approximated by mathematics describing the motion of a marble. In either case, it is not the particle that *is* the wave or the marble. It is the behavior of the particle which is being described by the mathematics of waves or marbles. In both cases, the mathematics gives the probability of finding the particle at a particular place with particular properties. The mathematics of marbles is very definite about this probability; the mathematics of waves gives the relative probabilities of the uncertain situation in terms of the amplitudes of a "probability wave."

This apparent duality is a perfectly normal state of affairs in this world. A woman is a woman is a woman. Yet in some circumstances she behaves like an animal and happily in others, like an angel.

RELATIVISTIC EFFECTS

Electrons which have been accelerated through 10^5 volts (perhaps in a dentist's x-ray machine) and thus have an energy of 10^5 ev will have a velocity about 100 times greater than the electron in the preceding section. Their wavelength is then smaller by a factor of 100. However, this simple arithmetic is not very applicable even at this low energy. The velocity of light is 3×10^8 m/sec and at the point where a particle has a velocity of $\frac{1}{10}$ of this, there has been a relativistic increase in mass of about $\frac{1}{2}\%$.

Many of the reactions that take place with particles occur at velocities very close to the speed of light, and so relativistic mechanics is the natural tool for describing the interactions. The particular relations useful for our purpose are these:

(1) $E_0 = m_0 c^2$.

Energy and rest mass are easily convertible. Here E_0 is the rest mass energy and m_0 is the mass of an object in its own rest frame.

If m_0 is expressed in kilograms, c is velocity of light in m/sec, then E is in joules (watt-seconds).*   There are 1.6×10^{-19} joule in one electron volt. Typical mass-energy unit relations are:

$$m_{\text{electron}} = 9 \times 10^{-31} \text{ kg} = 0.51 \text{ Mev},$$

$$m_{\text{proton}} = 1.6 \times 10^{-27} \text{ kg} = 931 \text{ Mev} \approx 1 \text{ Bev},$$

$$m_{1 \text{ gm of } H_2O} = 10^{-3} \text{ kg} = 5.4 \times 10^{26} \text{ Mev}$$

$$= 9 \times 10^{13} \text{ joules}$$

$$\approx \text{output of Niagara Falls for 10 hours.}$$

$$(2) \quad m = \frac{m_0}{\sqrt{1 - (v^2/c^2)}} = \frac{m_0}{\sqrt{1 - \beta^2}}.$$

The mass of an object is a function of the velocity of the object with respect to the observer. The *observed* mass is m; the mass in the *object's* rest frame is m_0. If:

$$\beta = \frac{v}{c} = \frac{1}{10}, \quad \text{then} \quad \frac{m}{m_0} = 1.005;$$

$$\beta = \frac{v}{c} = \frac{1}{2}, \quad \text{then} \quad \frac{m}{m_0} = 1.13;$$

$$\beta = \frac{v}{c} = \frac{9}{10}, \quad \text{then} \quad \frac{m}{m_0} = 1.65.$$

Experimental evidence for this increase is manifold. For instance, in electron-electron collisions at low energy, the tracks as seen in a cloud chamber always have an angle of 90° between them. This is a necessary feature of billiard ball collisions between objects of equal mass. But if the bombarding electron has high energy (of the order of, or greater than, $\frac{1}{2}$ Mev = its rest mass), then the opening angle between tracks is less than 90° and follows the appropriate dynamics for a collision between two particles with different masses.

In Bev circular particle accelerators, the particles rapidly come close to the speed of light. Each time they circle the machine, they receive the same amount of energy, and yet their velocity hardly changes. The energy is going into increased mass. The momentum of the particles is therefore increasing and this must be matched with an increase of the magnetic guide field which forces them to follow a curved path.

$$(3) \quad E = mc^2 = \frac{m_0 c^2}{\sqrt{1 - (v^2/c^2)}} = \frac{m_0 c^2}{\sqrt{1 - \beta^2}}.$$

This expression for the *total* energy E is always correct. E is then compounded of rest-mass energy plus kinetic energy. The denominator can be expanded in a binomial series.

$$\left(1 - \frac{v^2}{c^2}\right)^{-1/2} = 1 + \frac{1}{2}\frac{v^2}{c^2} + \frac{(\frac{1}{2} \times \frac{3}{2})}{2!}\frac{v^4}{c^4} + \frac{(\frac{1}{2} \times \frac{3}{2} \times \frac{5}{2})}{3!}\frac{v^6}{c^6} + \cdots$$

---

* A hundred-watt bulb uses 100 joules in one second.

The expansion thus begins:

$$E = m_0 c^2 + \tfrac{1}{2} m_0 v^2 + \tfrac{3}{8} m_0 v^2 \frac{v^2}{c^2} + \cdots$$

Obviously the first term is the rest-mass energy, which in classical physics always cancels out of any reactions and so can be ignored. The second term is the one we usually call kinetic energy. For ordinary velocities, the higher terms are completely negligible.

$$(4)\quad \Delta t = \frac{\Delta t_0}{\sqrt{1 - (v^2/c^2)}} = \frac{\Delta t_0}{\sqrt{1 - \beta^2}}.$$

The observed length of time interval is Δt; in the object's rest frame the interval is Δt_0. Relativistic dilation of time is seldom a problem with electron reactions, but we shall see that it is of vital importance for phenomena in-

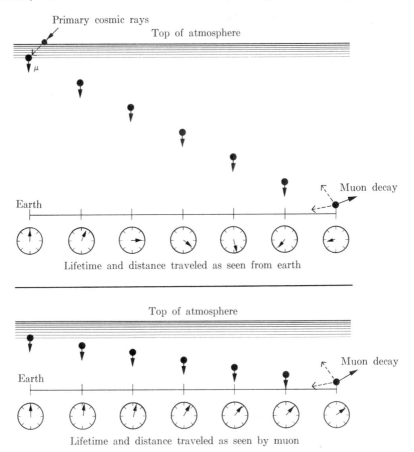

Fig. 20. Relativistic dilation of time for muon decay. In our reference frame the muon travels 20 miles and lives abnormally long. In the muon reference frame, the muon decays in its normal short lifetime, but, to the earth, the distance it travels appears very short.

volving other particles. Here again, the experimental proof is solid. Particles which would normally decay in a couple of millionths of a second may last hundreds of times as long. While you have been reading this page, more than one such particle, muons, have undoubtedly gone through you. If their clocks were not slowed by their high velocities, they would have decayed 20 miles or so up near the top of the atmosphere, not far from where they were created (Fig. 20).

This effect has nothing to do with the nature of the particle. It could happen to a meson or a man. Time itself is different in the speeding system compared with the stationary one. As can be seen from the energy formulas, however, there is considerably less energy involved in accelerating a particle than a man. There would seem to be no immediate prospect of providing a ripe young age for an astronaut.

HEISENBERG'S UNCERTAINTY PRINCIPLE

There is yet another important fact of life concerned with particle measurements. It is not always possible to measure—and so know—two properties of a particle, both with infinite precision. This is not just a matter of failing to have a sensitive enough meter of some kind. There is in principle, as well as in practice, a limit to the precision with which we can measure the position of a particle at the same time that we measure the momentum. Of course, every time any measurement is made of the position of some object a certain amount of error is involved. If you judge the position by eye of a scribe mark on the floor of a room you might guess the distance between it and a wall to within half a foot: $x = 3$ ft; $\Delta x = \pm\frac{1}{2}$ ft, where Δx describes not any mistake made but simply your assigned limits of accuracy. With a meter stick, the precision could be much greater: $x = 1$ meter; $\Delta x = \pm 2$ mm. If there were some reason to attain greater accuracy it could be done. The distance between two scribe marks on the standard meter stick in Paris was measured by Michelson in terms of the number of wavelengths of a particular spectral line of visible light. His accuracy with this technique was better than one part in a million: $x = 2 \times 10^6 \lambda$; $\Delta x = \pm 1\lambda$.

Even though practical considerations might rule out the extension of such efforts, it would seem that there should be no limit in principle to attaining greater accuracy. The measuring probe, of course, must be smaller than the Δx required. To do better than Michelson, it would be necessary to use light (or particles!) with smaller wavelength than visible light. Blue light with $\lambda = 4 \times 10^{-7}$ meter would be a little better than red with $\lambda = 7 \times 10^{-7}$ meter. In some microscopes this color effect is taken advantage of by using blue light to increase their resolution. Ultraviolet microscopes have been constructed, but the most widely used type is the electron microscope. The wavelength of the electrons in such a machine is about 2×10^{-9} meter, a hundred times better than can be obtained with visible light. Actually, resolution of even the best electron microscope is not so good as this, because of practical considerations of construction. To get even finer resolution, we need particles or light of yet smaller wavelength. But to get particles with smaller wavelength, we must increase their momentum: $\lambda = h/p$. The same problem faces us when we use light. The amount of energy in each photon of light is $E = h\nu = hc/\lambda$, where E is the energy in joules, h is Planck's constant, ν is the frequency of light in cycles per second, and λ is the wavelength in meters. As we go from radio to radar to infrared to visible to ultraviolet to x-rays to γ-rays, we deal with photons with greater and greater energy and with more of the behavior we normally associate with particles. Light does, of course, carry momentum. (Comet tails are blown away from the sun by photons and other particles emitted from the sun.) The amount of momentum is

$$p = \frac{E}{c} = \frac{h\nu}{c} = \frac{h}{\lambda}.$$

But this is just the expression we find for any other kind of particle!

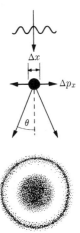

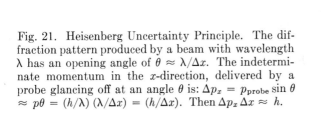

Fig. 21. Heisenberg Uncertainty Principle. The diffraction pattern produced by a beam with wavelength λ has an opening angle of $\theta \approx \lambda/\Delta x$. The indeterminate momentum in the x-direction, delivered by a probe glancing off at an angle θ is: $\Delta p_x = p_{\text{probe}} \sin \theta \approx p\theta = (h/\lambda)(\lambda/\Delta x) = (h/\Delta x)$. Then $\Delta p_x \Delta x \approx h$.

If the measuring probe has higher momentum as we decrease the wavelength, we can still measure the position of a tiny object as accurately as we choose, but in doing so we knock it away with the probe (Fig. 21). In measuring position we add an unknown amount of momentum to the object. The unknown momentum is *perpendicular* to the original direction of the wave probe. Instead of casting a sharp shadow of the object which would determine the position of the object exactly, the wave probe necessarily forms a diffraction pattern. Any particular photon (or other probe particle) can fall anywhere within the diffraction pattern in a completely indeterminate way. The opening angle for the maximum of the diffraction pattern is $\theta \approx \lambda/\Delta x$. The wavelength of the probe is λ and the indeterminate size of the object (either the vagueness of its edge, or more usually, the whole diameter) is Δx. Of course, the probe particle can also be deflected at an angle two or three times this large and land in one of the outer fringes of the diffraction pattern. Most, however, fall in the central maximum. A small wavelength of the probe produces a small diffraction pattern. But, as a result of the small wavelength, the probe carries higher momentum. This compensates for the smaller angle of deflection, producing a sideways impulse independent of the wavelength.

The dilemma is summarized by Heisenberg's Uncertainty Relationship. A more careful analysis of the uncertainties leads to a slightly lower limit for the product than the one derived in Fig. 21.

$$\Delta x \, \Delta p_x \geq \frac{h}{2\pi} = \hbar \approx 1 \times 10^{-34} \, \text{j·sec.}$$

In words, the product of the uncertainty in position and the uncertainty in momentum must always be equal to or greater than Planck's constant divided by 2π. This actually follows from our formula for the momentum of a particle, $p = h/\lambda$. In a glancing collision of a probe particle with an object, an appreciable fraction of its momentum, p, may be given to the object in a direction perpendicular to the original probe direction. Then that fraction, $\Delta p \approx p$, is the uncertainty in momentum of the object after the measurement. The position uncertainty Δx cannot be much less than the measuring wavelength λ. Since for the particle $p = h/\lambda$, for the object after the collision, $\Delta p_x \approx h/\Delta x$. If angular momentum were not quantized, that is, if Planck's constant were zero, both position and momentum could be measured simultaneously with infinite precision. This world would not be this world at all in that case.

Heisenberg's principle also applies to other pairs of quantities which in classical science can in principle be known together with infinite precision. Instead of linear position, x, choose angular position, θ. Then $\Delta \theta \times \Delta L \geq \hbar$, where $\Delta \theta$ is the uncertainty in angle of a rotating system and ΔL is the uncertainty in *angular* momentum. We have claimed, however, that for atomic systems, the angular momentum associated with the orbital arrangement of the electron is very definite. The electron spin itself is $\frac{1}{2}\hbar$, with no uncertainty at all. (It may be pointed in or out of line, but the magnitude remains the same.) In all these cases, however, Heisenberg's principle accurately predicts the experimental situation. Since $\Delta L = 0$ (no uncertainty), then θ is undetermined. The angular position is in principle, and in practice, completely unknown.

Another pair of variables is of importance in particle physics: $\Delta E \times \Delta t \geq \hbar$, where ΔE is the uncertainty in the energy of a system *at the time we measure it* and Δt is the uncertainty in the time of the measurement. One is tempted to say that ΔE is the uncertainty with which we *know* the energy E, implying that actually the system has a definite energy. This is a deluding thought. Once again, if in principle something cannot be measured, then the question as to whether or not it exists is meaningless.

How can we measure the energy of an excited state of a system? The most general method is to let the system return to normal and see how much energy comes out. A collision, perhaps, throws an atom into an excited state, with one of the electrons in a nonstable position. The uncertainty of the energy of the

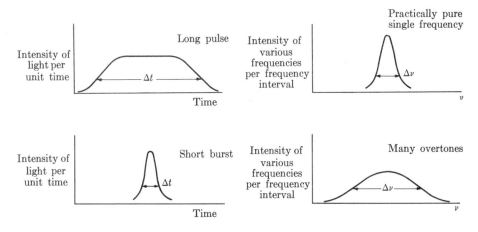

Fig. 22. Relationship between duration of light pulse and spread of frequencies.

system presents no problem, however, until the time when we receive the information. As the atom returns to normal, as the electron hops down into place, a photon is emitted. It carries energy $E = h\nu$, and this implies that it has a definite wavelength $\lambda = c/\nu$. However, the photon was emitted in a time of about 10^{-8} sec for an ordinary atomic transition. Before then there was no photon, and after that the electromagnetic vibrations stop coming from the atom. Figure 22 shows how a meter might record this situation. But a train of sine waves has a definite frequency, is a pure tone, only if it has been emitted forever and will continue indefinitely. A short burst of oscillations must have overtones associated with it. These are higher frequencies which, when mixed with the main note, produce a beginning and end to the pulse. The shorter the duration, the more important the overtones. Instead of a single sharp wavelength, a narrow band of wavelengths is produced. The sharp spectral line has width.

In the case of visible light where $\Delta t \approx 10^{-8}$ sec, we have

$$\Delta E \times \Delta t \geq \hbar \approx 10^{-34}\ \text{j·sec},$$
$$\Delta E \approx 10^{-26}\ \text{joule} \approx 10^{-7}\ \text{ev}.$$

This seems like a small uncertainty, indeed. Since the energy of a visible photon is about 2 ev, it appears that the energy is definite to one part in 10 million. But spectroscopy can attain precision such that this is observed as the natural line width. The uncertainty in frequency is $\Delta\nu \approx 10^8$ cycles/sec and the irreducible width of the spectral line is $\Delta\lambda \approx 0.001$ angstroms(Å), or about 0.3 millionth of the length of the whole spectrum from red to blue.

We shall have occasion to deal with particles or excited states with lifetimes as small as 10^{-22} sec. In this case $\Delta E \approx 10^{-12}$ joule ≈ 10 Mev. Uncertainties of this size can play dominant roles in certain particle reactions.

Section 4.   Chart of the Particles Stable against Decay through Nuclear Forces

ORGANIZATION AND FAMILIAR FEATURES

Let us now take a census of the relatively stable particles, noting along the way the very short and recent history of this subject (Fig. 23). At this point we discriminate against the even more recent discoveries of particles which decay in times less than 10^{-22} sec. These are not stable against decay through the strong nuclear interaction. Their discovery and significance is described in Section 8.

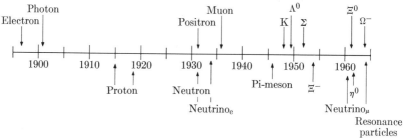

Fig. 23. Time table for discovery of particles. For some of the particles, there is a difference between the date of first observation and the date of understanding the nature of the particle. For instance, although the muon was observed in 1937, its significance was not understood until ten years later. The existence of the neutrino was postulated in 1933, but the inverse beta decay, which it can cause, was not observed until 1956.

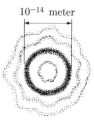

Fig. 24. An electron confined to a nucleus would have an uncertainty in energy far greater than the nuclear binding energy. If it were forced to have small enough momentum to be bound, its position would be uncertain by an amount far greater than the nuclear size.

Electrons have been known for seventy years although some of their properties have been discovered only since World War II. Protons were recognized about the time of World War I, but the existence of neutrons was not suspected until the depression days of 1932. Until then it was thought that the atomic nucleus contained enough protons to make up the atomic weight and enough electrons to cancel out half or more of the positive charge, leaving net charge equal to the atomic number. For instance, $_6C^{12}$, the common isotope of carbon, has atomic weight 12 and atomic number 6. The old explanation called for 12 protons and 6 electrons in the carbon nucleus.

Among other troubles with the nuclear electron theory, the Heisenberg uncertainty relation will not allow electrons to be confined in something as small as an atomic nucleus (Fig. 24). If the electron is in the nucleus, then the uncertainty in its position must be no greater than the nuclear diameter. This defines the minimum uncertainty in its momentum. Thus,

$$\Delta x \times \Delta p \geq \hbar,$$
$$10^{-14} \text{ m} \times \Delta p \approx 10^{-34} \text{ j·sec},$$
$$\Delta p \approx 10^{-20} \text{ kg} \cdot \text{m/sec}.$$

With the mass of the electron equal to 9×10^{-31} kg, the nonrelativistic expression for momentum, $m_0 v$, would give a velocity $v \approx 10^{10}$ m/sec. Since the velocity of light is 3×10^8 m/sec, it is apparent that relativistic formulas must be used. The total energy, including rest mass, of an object is given by

$$E_T = \sqrt{(m_0 c^2)^2 + c^2 p^2},$$

where p is the momentum and c is, as usual, the velocity of light. A convenient way to present this graphically is

If the rest mass energy, $m_0 c^2$, is small compared with the motion energy, cp, we can use the approximation $E_T \approx cp$. The kinetic energy is $E_K = E_T - m_0 c^2$. In the case of the confined electron we can ignore this difference too and simply ask: how much energy is associated with the electron's momentum uncertainty?

$$\Delta p \approx 10^{-20} \text{ kg} \cdot \text{m/sec},$$
$$\Delta E \approx cp = 3 \times 10^8 \times 10^{-20} = 3 \times 10^{-12} \text{ joule}.$$

Since 1.6×10^{-19} joule $= 1$ ev, we have

$$\Delta E \approx 20 \text{ Mev}.$$

Thus we were justified in ignoring $m_0 c^2$ which for the electron is only $\frac{1}{2}$ Mev.

If the intrinsic uncertainty of the energy of the electron when it is confined to the nucleus is 20 Mev, then it must be bound by an even greater energy if the nucleus is to remain stable. But the missing mass of nuclei which accounts for binding energy is such that the nuclear binding *per particle* is never greater than about 8 Mev.

A proton in the nucleus has just as great an uncertainty in momentum, but since it is nearly 2000 times as massive as the electron, this corresponds to much less uncertainty in the energy. In 1932 Chadwick proved that the neutral emanation from beryllium bombarded with alpha particles could not be x-rays, but

CHART OF THE PARTICLES STABLE AGAINST STRONG NUCLEAR DECAY

CLASS	NAME	PARTICLES	ANTIPARTICLES
		$S = -3$	$S = +3$
	Omega Hyperon	Ω^-	$\overline{\Omega}^+$
	$I=0$ Spin $= 3/2\hbar$	$S = -2$	$S = +2$
	Cascade Hyperon	Ξ^0 Ξ^-	$\overline{\Xi}^+$ $\overline{\Xi}^0$
	$I = 1/2$ Spin $= 1/2\ \hbar$	$I_3 = +\frac{1}{2}$ $I_3 = -\frac{1}{2}$	$I_3 = +\frac{1}{2}$ $I_3 = -\frac{1}{2}$
BARYONS Strongly Interacting Fermions (Spin $=$ half-integral)		$S = -1$	$S = +1$
	Sigma Hyperon	Σ^+ Σ^0 Σ^-	$\overline{\Sigma}^+$ $\overline{\Sigma}^0$ $\overline{\Sigma}^-$
	$I = 1$ Spin $= 1/2\ \hbar$	$I_3 = +1$ $I_3 = 0$ $I_3 = -1$	$I_3 = +1$ $I_3 = 0$ $I_3 = -1$
	Lambda Hyperon	$S = -1$ Λ^0	$S = +1$ $\overline{\Lambda}^0$
	$I = 0$ Spin $= 1/2\ \hbar$		
		Baryon charge center	Anti baryon charge center
	Nucleon (Proton-Neutron)	p^+ n^0	$\overline{n}^0$ $\overline{p}^-$
	$I = 1/2$ Spin $= 1/2\ \hbar$	$I_3 = +1/2$ $I_3 = -1/2$	$I_3 = +1/2$ $I_3 = -1/2$
MESONS Strongly Interacting Bosons (Spin $= 0$)	η-Meson	η^0	
	$I = 0$		
	K-Meson	K^+ K^0	$\overline{K}^0$ $\overline{K}^-$
	$I = 1/2$	$I_3 = +1/2$ $I_3 = -1/2$	$I_3 = +1/2$ $I_3 = -1/2$
		$S = +1$ $S = -1$	
	Pi-Meson	π^+ π^0 π^-	
	$I = 1$	$I_3 = +1$ $I_3 = 0$ $I_3 = -1$	
LEPTONS Weakly Interacting Fermions (Spin $= 1/2\ \hbar$)	Muon	μ^-	μ^+
	Electron	e^-	e^+ (Positron)
	Neutrino-muon	ν_μ	$\overline{\nu}_\mu$
	Neutrino-electron	ν_e	$\overline{\nu}_e$
MASSLESS (Spin $= 1\hbar$) **BOSONS** (Spin $= 2\hbar$)	Photon	γ	
	Graviton?		

CHART OF THE PARTICLES (CONT.)

REST MASS IN MEV	HALF LIFE IN SECONDS	DECAY SCHEMES	
1676	$\sim 10^{-10}$	$\Omega^- \to \Lambda^0 + K^-$	
$\Xi^\pm \approx 1320$	$.9 \times 10^{-10}$	$\Xi^- \to \Lambda^0 + \pi^-$	
$\Xi^0 \approx 1310$	1.0×10^{-10}	$\Xi^0 \to \Lambda^0 + \pi^0$	
	$.6 \times 10^{-10}$	$\Sigma^+ \to p^+ + \pi^0$	(50 %)
		$\to n^0 + \pi^+$	(50 %)
≈ 1190		$\Sigma^0 \to \Lambda^0 + \gamma$	
	1.2×10^{-10}	$\Sigma^- \to n^0 + \pi^-$	
1115	1.7×10^{-10}	$\Lambda^0 \to p^+ + \pi^-$	(67 %)
		$\to n^0 + \pi^0$	(33 %)
n 939.5	$.7 \times 10^3$	$n^0 \to p^+ + e^- + \bar{\nu}$	
P 938.2	Stable		
		$\eta^0 \to \pi^+ + \pi^- + \pi^0$	
548	$< 10^{-16}$	$\to \pi^0 + e^+ + \nu$	(5 %)
		$\to \pi^0 + \mu^+ + \nu$	(5 %)
		$K^+ \to \mu^+ + \nu$	(64 %)
		$\to \pi^+ + \pi^0$	(19 %)
		$\to 2\pi^+ + \pi^-$	(6 %)
$(K^- = K^+)$ 494	$.8 \times 10^{-8}$	$\to \pi^+ + 2\pi^0$	(2 %)
K^0 } K_1^0	0.7×10^{-10}	$K_1^0 \to \pi^+ + \pi^-$	$(\approx 34 \%)$
$\bar{K}^0$ } 498		$\to 2\pi^0$	$(\approx 16 \%)$
K_2^0	4×10^{-8}	$\to \pi^+ + \pi^- + \pi^0$	(7 %)
		$\to 3\pi^0$	
		$K_2^0 \to \pi^\pm + \mu^\mp + \bar{\nu}$	(19 %)
		$\to \pi^\pm + e^\mp + \nu$	(24 %)
π^- 140	1.8×10^{-8}	$\pi^- \to \mu^- + \bar{\nu}$	
π^0 135	0.7×10^{-16}	$\pi^0 \to \gamma + \gamma \quad (\pi^0 \to \gamma + e^+ + e^- \quad 1\%)$	
π^+ 140	1.8×10^{-8}	$\pi^+ \to \mu^+ + \nu \quad (\pi^+ \to e^+ + \nu \quad .01\%)$	
105.7	1.5×10^{-6}	$\mu^- \to e^- + \nu + \bar{\nu}$	
0.51	Stable		
0	The neutrinos associated with $\mu^\pm$ are different from those with $e^\pm$		
0			
0	Stable		
0	Stable	Not Detected	

must consist of particles about as heavy as the proton. (Alpha particles consist of a combination of two protons and two neutrons. They are emitted spontaneously from many natural radioactive materials. This same tightly bound combination is also the nucleus of the helium atom.) When one of these neutral particles from the beryllium strikes a hydrogen nucleus (a proton) in a cloud chamber, the recoil proton takes off with energy and angle appropriate for a billiard ball collision between objects of equal mass.

Insofar as man comprehended, all the world of 1932 was made up of just three particles: protons and neutrons in the nuclei of atoms, and electrons in the orbital shells. Carbon-12, for instance, had six protons, six neutrons, and six electrons. Of course, even then the situation was known to be more complicated. Photons, or light, had particle properties, even as the other three had wave properties under the proper circumstances. Furthermore, in 1933 Blackett and Anderson discovered a positive electron in cloud chamber pictures. In 1935, Yukawa proposed that there might be a particle-like agent of the nuclear force, the meson.

By 1950 a great number of strange events had been observed by instruments exposed to cosmic rays. There were V-tracks and V_1-, V_2-, and many other variations. It was not at all clear whether or not a phenomenon observed in a cloud chamber on Mount Wilson was the same as had been observed by photographic emulsions during a balloon flight over England. In fact, it was not even clear whether some of these freak phenomena were due to new particles or were just statistical variations of better known events.

It was at this point that the big accelerators started making their contribution. First the Cosmotron at Brookhaven National Laboratory and then the Bevatron in Berkeley started producing the strange events on command and in great abundance. Although most of the particles were first observed in cosmic-ray experiments, their properties are most easily probed with the big machines. Indeed, one of the roles of accelerator experiments has been to explain away strange events which were previously thought to be due to new particles.

The chart of the particles (pages 32–33) summarizes the state of knowledge about stable and pseudostable particles in the spring of 1964. Remember first, that this is a classification scheme, far more than a list but less than a theory. The classifying divisions are based on the attributes, or parameters, of the particles. In the last chapter we shall examine other classification schemes which include the new resonance particles.

THE PARAMETERS

1. Mass. The particles are listed vertically according to mass. The mass of a particle is usually measured in terms of the energy it takes to produce it. This is given in Mev, which may be changed to joules or kilograms with the conversion constants already derived and summarized in the Appendix. Note the positions and values of the familiar trio: electron at about $\frac{1}{2}$ Mev, and proton and neutron at almost 1 Bev.

2. Particle, antiparticles. Most of the particles have antiparticles with identical mass and spin but opposite electric charge and strangeness number (to be described under Article 5). They are identified in symbols by placing a bar over the letter. Thus the proton is p and the antiproton $\bar{p}$. The antiparticles are just as stable (or unstable) as their counterparts and so far as we know could form a complete antiuniverse. Perhaps some galaxies are composed of antimatter. Which is the particle and which the antiparticle is simply a question of local prevalence.

It might seem that antineutrons would have no distinguishing characteristics since they have zero net charge just like neutrons. The distinction is clear, however, in high-energy experiments where they are produced and detected. When they collide with a nucleus of "real" matter, they are annihilated along with a proton or neutron. The rest mass of particle and antiparticle turns into other forms, the rest mass and kinetic energy of mesons.

Plate III shows such an annihilation between an antiproton and a proton from the hydrogen in a bubble chamber. The inverse process of production takes place if enough energy is supplied to make up the total rest mass of the particle and its antiparticle. For an electron-positron pair this requires a little over one Mev. Plate I shows such a pair creation by a γ-ray. In the magnetic field of the cloud chamber, the negative electron circles in one direction while the positive electron is forced in the opposite sense. The x-ray or γ-ray which produced this event left no trail in the chamber because it did not interact with anything until finally it yielded all its energy to the electron pair. Any energy of the γ-ray greater than one Mev went into the kinetic energy of the electrons.

Three of the particles serve as their own antiparticles. These are the photon, the π^0-meson, and the η^0-meson, all with zero electric charge and zero strangeness.

3. Spin and statistics. There are four main horizontal groupings, each with its class name. Two consist of fermions, particles with spin $\frac{1}{2}$, $\frac{3}{2}$, $\frac{5}{2}$, etc., which must obey the Pauli exclusion principle, and two contain bosons (named after Bose, who analyzed this feature of their behavior) which have integer spin, $s = 0, 1, 2$, etc. The fermions are subject to a conservation principle. They can be created or destroyed only in conjunction with an antiparticle from their same class. When an electron is emitted from a nucleus, for instance, it is created out of surplus energy but must be accompanied by an antineutrino. An anti-electron, or positron, would satisfy this requirement just as well, but, of course, would defeat the charge reduction which induced the decay. Similarly, when a γ-ray produces a positron-electron pair, the antiparticle requirement could be satisfied with a positron-neutrino pair, but that would not conserve electric charge.

The conservation principle does not extend between the two classes of fermions. The nucleonlike fermion particles are called *baryons*, the heavy ones. Members of the light group of fermions are called *leptons*. The total number of baryons remains constant and so, apparently, does the total number of leptons.

No such principle of conservation applies to the bosons. So long as charge, angular momentum, etc., are conserved, the bosons can be created without regard to their antiparticles. Photons, for instance, can be boiled endlessly out of a hot tungsten filament. In some respects, these bosons can be considered as agents or messengers of the nuclear, gravitational, and electromagnetic fields, although they are also particles as far as our arbitrary definition is concerned. As we shall see, in the case of the strong nuclear force there is probably no reason to call any one of the particles the source and another the agent.

The group behavior of the two classes was first described in terms of statistical effects. Fermions obey Fermi-Dirac statistics; bosons follow Bose-Einstein statistics.

4. Isotopic spin. In two strokes of classification, we have sorted out all of the building blocks of nature into particles and antiparticles, and have fitted each into one of only four groups. But the members of each group can be further arranged to display similarities. Most of the particles can appear in various electric charge states: plus, minus, or zero. These are analogous to the isotopic groupings of the elements, atoms which have the same chemical properties but different numbers of neutrons in their nuclei. In the case of the particles, the members of isotopic triplets or doublets have only slightly different masses from their partners and, except for the electromagnetic effects, behave basically the same.

The best known isotopic partners are the proton and neutron. As we shall demonstrate in the next chapter, the nuclear forces seem to be the same for the two particles. It is useful to think of them as just different charge manifestations of the same particle—the *nucleon*. Here, then, is an isotopic *doublet*. The next heavier particle, Λ^0 (lambda), is a *singlet*; beyond that the Σ (sigma) is a *triplet*; the Ξ (xi, or the cascade particle) is a *doublet*; and the heaviest of all, Ω^- (omega), is a *singlet*.

A useful scheme has been developed to label these multiplets and to make it convenient to describe them mathematically. It is observed that there is an analogous situation in describing the spin of a particle. If a particle has spin 0, it can exist in only one orientation; spin $\frac{1}{2}$ yields two possibilities, $+\frac{1}{2}$ and $-\frac{1}{2}$; spin 1 can be arranged as a triplet, $+1$, 0, and -1. The general formula for the multiplicity is that there can be $(2s + 1)$ states. For instance, spin $\frac{3}{2}$ gives $[(2 \times \frac{3}{2}) + 1]$ or 4 states, $+\frac{3}{2}$, $+\frac{1}{2}$, $-\frac{1}{2}$, $-\frac{3}{2}$. There must always be a difference of one between possible spin orientations. Evidently there is no way for a particle to change spin orientation except in unit amounts. If an atom, for instance, gives off a photon of light in ordinary optical emission, there is a change of angular momentum in the atom of *one*, since the photon has spin *one*. When a nucleus or unstable particle emits a β-ray, it loses spin $\frac{1}{2}$, but because the leptons are conserved, there must be yet another spin loss of $\frac{1}{2}$ due to a neutrino, leading to a change of 0 or 1.

In a similar way we can use this mathematical notation to label the particle multiplets. They are assigned values of *isotopic spin*, I. Singlets have $I = 0$,

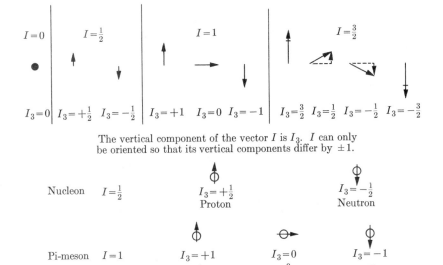

The vertical component of the vector I is I_3. I can only
be oriented so that its vertical components differ by ± 1.

Fig. 25. Rules for isotopic multiplets.

doublets have $I = \frac{1}{2}$, triplets have $I = 1$. At first, this labeling is just that, a game to be played with symbols. In complicated reactions it takes on a more profound aspect, allowing general laws to be stated in shorthand terms, as we shall see. The members of a multiplet are assigned particular values of the isotopic spin, as though they were represented by *components* of a vector which could rotate in space—isotopic spin space. Figure 25 illustrates this scheme, with the projection, I_3, of the isotopic spin vector assuming different values for the different members. For the proton, for instance $I_3 = +\frac{1}{2}$ and for the neutron, $I_3 = -\frac{1}{2}$. The total isotopic spin for the nucleon is still $\frac{1}{2}$, but it can be oriented in two ways even as can a particle with ordinary spin $\frac{1}{2}$. In a *magnetic* field, the ordinary spins are sorted out, because they exist at different energies, depending on whether the magnetic moment is with or against the field. The nuclear forces do not distinguish between members of an isotopic spin multiplet, but when the *electromagnetic* field is "turned on," differentiating charges, plus, minus, and zero, there is a separation measurable in terms of mass difference. These labels are useful only for the *baryons* and *mesons*. Although I-values could be assigned to the lepton multiplets, it would not help describe the processes in which they are involved.

If you have at this point, a feeling that this labeling scheme is arbitrary and artificial, you are partly right. The justification for Mendeléeff's table was that it worked. That is, it simplified the listing of known facts and predicted new ones. Patience! This scheme for the particles also works.

5. Strangeness. Having labeled the multiplets, we note a strange feature of this organization. The baryons are arranged in columns according to their electric charge: plus under plus, minus under minus, neutral under neutral. The electric charge centers of the multiplets do not, however, occur in the same vertical line. The electric charge center of the nucleon is at $+\frac{1}{2}$, halfway between positive proton and neutral neutron. The charge center of lambda zero is, of course, at 0. The triplet sigma is centered at 0, but the doublet xi has electric charge center at $-\frac{1}{2}$. The omega singlet is at charge -1.

If now we accept the nucleon pair as the most familiar among the baryons, we remark how *strange* it is that the other baryons do not center in charge around the nucleon center line. So strange is this that we assign *strangeness* numbers to the other baryons according to the scheme which is best observed on the chart. A displacement of charge center $\frac{1}{2}$ unit to the right from the arbitrary center line of the nucleons will be defined as corresponding to a strangeness of $S = -1$. Such is the case for the Λ^0 and the Σ. A displacement of one charge unit to the right means strangeness $S = -2$, as in the case of the cascade particle, Ξ. The Ω displacement of $1\frac{1}{2}$ units to the right implies $S = -3$.

The same construction is used for the mesons, only here the charge center of the pi-mesons, zero, is chosen for the normal charge center. This makes the K^+, K^0 doublet charge center $\frac{1}{2}$ unit to the *left* of zero. Strangeness of $S = +1$ is assigned to the doublet.

Since the charges of particles are reflected as in a mirror by the dividing line between particles and antiparticles, the antiparticles will have strangeness opposite in sign to their particle counterparts. Note that although the leptons might be arranged in a similar way, no strangeness numbers have been assigned to them, because no use has been found for dealing with them in this way.

Some usefulness for this game should be presented quickly. First of all, note that the charge of a particle is related to the strangeness, isotopic spin, and baryon number. This last name is simply an assignment of $b = +1$ for each baryon, -1 for each antibaryon, and 0 for anything else. Then the electric charge $Q = e(I_3 + b/2 + S/2)$, where e is the unit electric charge. For example, the proton has $I_3 = +\frac{1}{2}$, $b = +1$, and $S = 0$. Therefore its charge $Q = +e$. On the other hand, the antiproton has $I_3 = -\frac{1}{2}$, $b = -1$, and $S = 0$, leading to $Q = -e$. The K^+-meson has $I_3 = +\frac{1}{2}$, $b = 0$, and $S = +1$. Its charge is $Q = +e$. For a more complicated case, the neutral anti-xi particle has $I_3 = -\frac{1}{2}$, $b = -1$, and $S = +2$, yielding $Q = 0$.

There was more excuse than this for inventing strangeness numbers, of course. The original idea was a response to the problem of associated production of the new strange particles. One of the early triumphs of research at the Cosmotron was a demonstration in 1952 of something that had already been suspected. The hyperons and K-mesons were never produced singly in the high-energy particle collisions, but were always created in association with each other. A typical reaction is

$$\pi^- + p^+ \rightarrow \Lambda^0 + K^0$$
$$\qquad\qquad\quad \hookrightarrow \pi^+ + \pi^-$$
$$\qquad\quad \hookrightarrow p^+ + \pi^-$$

There is no apparent reason that the following reaction should not be seen:

$$\pi^- + p^+ \rightarrow \Lambda^0 + \pi^0.$$

But it never is. If (at least at these energies) a hyperon is produced, a K-meson must also be generated. There is a further mystery. Protons and π-mesons interact strongly. If a compound particle, such as the Λ^0, is going to decay into a proton and π, why does it not do so almost as soon as it is formed? We shall argue in the next section that the strange particles (those with strangeness numbers not equal to zero) live much longer than we would expect. Usually such stability is associated with a conservation law. If a reaction does not go, perhaps it is because to do so would violate the conservation of some quantity: energy, momentum, charge, etc.

Both the associated creation of the strange particles and their individual stability against immediate decay were the features that earned them the title "strange." Both features can be "explained" by insisting that the total *strangeness* involved in a *fast* particle reaction must remain constant. Since the hyperons all have negative strangeness, they can be produced only in association with K-mesons of positive strangeness. Of course, the production of two K-mesons, one positive and one negative, would also satisfy this requirement, and such reactions are commonly seen at the very high-energy accelerators. To produce such a K-meson pair requires enough extra and available collision energy to provide the rest mass—about 1000 Mev. Once a hyperon or K-meson is produced and gets beyond the influence of the collision, it cannot decay without changing its strangeness, since the decay products have strangeness zero. Thus in the fast nuclear processes, where total strangeness before and after a reaction must be the same, strange particles can be produced only in pairs; once produced and separated from each other, they must wait for some weaker interaction to allow them to decay.

The strangeness feature is sometimes referred to in terms of another name, hypercharge, with the symbol Y. Hypercharge is defined to be equal to twice the average charge of a multiplet. For mesons it is the same as the strangeness number, since the charge center for strangeness determination of mesons was taken at zero. For baryons, however, the charge center was taken to be that of the nucleon doublet at $+\frac{1}{2}$. Therefore, the hypercharge of the nucleon is $+1$, although its strangeness is 0. The relationship between hypercharge and strangeness is $Y = S + b$, where b is the baryon number. This makes the hypercharge of the Λ and Σ zero; the Ξ, -1; and the Ω, -2.

6. Decay times. As the chart shows, most of the particles are unstable. They decay according to the laws of probability made familiar in studies of natural radioactivity: the number of decays, ΔN, during an interval of time is proportional to the duration of the time interval, Δt, and to the number of particles present, $\Delta N = \lambda N \Delta t$, where λ is the proportionality constant. If there were originally N_0 particles present, then after a time t, the number remaining is $N = N_0 e^{-\lambda t}$. The nature of such an equation is that after a time $T_{1/2} = 0.69/\lambda$

only one-half of the original particles will be present, and after another $T_{1/2}$ only one-half of those will remain.

Many order-of-magnitude arguments about particle reactions and experimental response make use of the half-life, $T_{1/2}$, as though it were *the* lifetime. To be sure, after five half lives only 3% of the particles remain. However, this is a statistical affair and surprising, but normal, fluctuations can occur. Furthermore, the half lives given are for particles at rest in the observer's reference frame. If, relative to an observer, the particle is moving at a speed close to that of light, time dilation will increase the observed lifetime.

The only particles stable against decay *in vacuo* are the photon, graviton, neutrinos (so far as we know), electron, proton and their antiparticles. Of course, particle and antiparticle will always annihilate if they come into contact. Any particle will decay into a combination of lighter particles, providing that none of the conservation laws forbid it. These will be discussed in Section 6. The nature of these laws is largely discovered by observing which decay schemes occur and which do not. For instance, it is observed that none of the baryons decay into a combination of particles that does not include a baryon. The proton cannot decay into a number of mesons. Since no other law seems to forbid this, we hypothesize a law that the number of baryons must be conserved. Thus the "explanation" of the stability of the proton is the law of conservation of baryons!

Section 5.   The Interactions

All of the phenomena observed in high-energy physics experiments can be explained in terms of the behavior of a few classes of particles. The simplification is even greater than this, however, for these particles have only four types of interactions. In other words, we now know only four physical forces in the world. Normally we speak of many more than this—chemical, muscular, spring, electrical, molecular, gravitational, etc. All of these can be classified as examples of the four basic ones, and indeed in everyday life we are concerned with only two.

In exploring the nature of any force, we ask: what kind of objects participate in the interaction, or what is the "charge" that acts as a source; how does the interaction depend on the distance between charges, and in what direction is the force; does the interaction also depend on the relative velocity or on the orientation of the participants; what is the strength of the force relative to the other three under comparable conditions of interest; and finally, how does the interaction propagate itself through space—is there an agent or messenger and does the effect take time or is it instantaneous?

GRAVITY

The first force that any of us discover is gravity. It pulls us out of cribs and chairs at an early age. It also holds the moon and earth together, keeps the planets in their solar orbits, and binds ten billion stars to form our galaxy. In Einstein's theory of general relativity, gravity becomes the warping of space itself and the warping agent is mass. Newton, also, back in 1666, proposed that mass was the source or charge of gravitational attraction. His venerable formula which still describes most gravitation effects accurately enough is:

$$F = G\,\frac{mM}{r^2}.$$

Here F is the force, always attractive in the case of gravity, between two objects with masses m and M, a distance r apart. The constant G depends only on the units used for the variables, whether feet, meters, furlongs, or what have you. It is assumed that the objects are small compared with r so that there is no question about how to measure the separation (Fig. 26). Although it is not at all obvious, it turns out that if the objects are spheres not enclosed in each other, with the mass density a function only of the radius, the distance should be measured center to center. Then the formula is precise even though the objects are nearly as large as the separation. If the masses are measured in kilograms and the distance in meters, then the force is given in *newtons* (appropriately enough). A one-pound object *weighs* (is attracted to the earth by a force of) about $4\frac{1}{2}$ newtons. In this system of units G equals 6.7×10^{-11} n $\cdot$ m^2/kg^2.

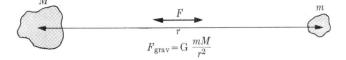

$$F_{\text{grav}} = G\,\frac{mM}{r^2}$$

There are some remarkable facts about this formula which are often hidden by its symmetry, simplicity, and (most of all) by its familiarity. First of all, the mass which serves as the charge of the interaction is the same kind of mass as in the defining equation $F = ma$. Gravitational mass is the same thing as inertial mass! This is at first thought (or second, if the first left you cold) an astonishing coincidence. Why should the resistance of matter to a change in its motion, its inertia, have anything to do with the phenomenon of matter attracting other matter? The gravitational effect does not depend on the color, size, electric charge, or any other condition of an object, but only on the magnitude of its inertia. So surprising did Einstein find this situation that he concluded it must be a reflection of something more profound. The equivalence of inertial and gravitational mass became the basic hypothesis of the theory of general relativity.

Now note the exponential powers of the variables. The force is proportional to the first power of the inertial mass, not to the square or the 1.34 power. If it were not so, Galileo's famous stones dropping from the Leaning Tower of Pisa would not have struck earth at the same time (Fig. 27). Thus, a 2 kg stone has twice the weight (force of attraction to earth) as a 1 kg stone. But its inertia is also exactly twice as great, and so in spite of the greater force on it, the acceleration is the same as on the light stone.

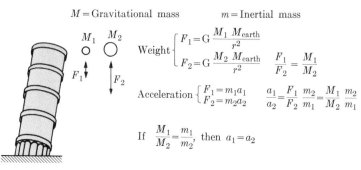

M = Gravitational mass m = Inertial mass

$$\text{Weight} \begin{cases} F_1 = G\dfrac{M_1\, M_{\text{earth}}}{r^2} \\ F_2 = G\dfrac{M_2\, M_{\text{earth}}}{r^2} \end{cases} \qquad \dfrac{F_1}{F_2} = \dfrac{M_1}{M_2}$$

$$\text{Acceleration} \begin{cases} F_1 = m_1 a_1 \\ F_2 = m_2 a_2 \end{cases} \qquad \dfrac{a_1}{a_2} = \dfrac{F_1}{F_2}\dfrac{m_2}{m_1} = \dfrac{M_1}{M_2}\dfrac{m_2}{m_1}$$

$$\text{If} \quad \dfrac{M_1}{M_2} = \dfrac{m_1}{m_2}, \text{ then } a_1 = a_2$$

FIG. 27. Equivalence of gravitational and inertial masses. If gravitational mass is proportional to inertial mass, all objects (in a vacuum) will fall with the same acceleration.

The force is inversely proportional to the distance of separation *squared*. Precision experiments have shown that this exponential factor of two is exact to better than one part in a billion. It is, from one point of view, simply a reflection of our three-dimensional universe. Any influence which spreads out uniformly in all directions from a point source without decaying or being absorbed must have its effect depend on the inverse square of the distance to the source. Light intensity from a small lamp behaves the same way. For large masses and over large distances, this formula cannot explain all observed effects and we must reinterpret observations in terms of Einstein's general theory.

The directional properties of this force are fortunately simple. The attraction between two objects is directed in the same direction as the line which joins them. This is so straightforward, literally and figuratively, that we would not expect it to be any other way, except that other forces are sometimes perpendicular to the joining line. Furthermore, the gravitational force does not depend on the velocity of the two masses, or their spins, or their angular orientation.

As for the intrinsic strength of the interaction, everyday experience testifies to the large effects of gravity. Yet in comparing the magnitudes of the four forces, we must take some standard situation. On the days when human weight seems intolerable, we must remember that it represents the attraction between some 10^{29} protons and neutrons within our body to over 10^{51} nucleons in the earth. True, the separation is large (6×10^6 meters, the radius of the earth) but this is not so important since an inverse square is comparatively a slowly varying function. Our standard comparison situation shall be the interaction between two nucleons separated only by a nucleon diameter, 10^{-15} meter. Under these circumstances, the gravitational attraction does not fare so well.

The gravitational force between nucleons is

$$F = G\frac{mM}{r^2} = 6.7 \times 10^{-11}\frac{(1.7 \times 10^{-27})^2}{(10^{-15})^2} \approx 2 \times 10^{-34}\text{ newton.}$$

We shall compare this force with that produced by the electrical repulsion and the strong nuclear attraction. In the meantime, consider that the energy involved in the escape of two nucleons from their mutual gravitational attraction is only about 2×10^{-49} joule or 10^{-30} ev. Compared with the nuclear binding energy of about 10 million ev/particle, the gravitational effect is clearly infinitesimal. It plays no role in particle reactions and achieves significance only when the number of interacting particles and the distances involved are vast. Then, of course, it holds the universe together.

Although for the business of this world we know all about gravity and have for over three hundred years, we really know very little about how the effect is propagated through space. Men once thought that the planets were guided in their courses by celestial crystal channels. Newton changed all that with his cold mathematics of action at a distance and never mind the mechanism. In the nineteenth century, forces were thought to be propagated by fields, space warped for particular effects. In the twentieth century these fields are explained in terms of, and become synonymous with, agents or messengers which actually propagate the effect. The photon, or light, for example, is the agent of the electromagnetic field. From this point of view, gravitation can be explained in terms of the interactions of "gravitons." Their mass must be zero, and therefore their velocity must be that of light. Since, as we calculated, the strength of the gravitational field is extremely weak, it would seem that the detection of individual gravitons is beyond our techniques now, and perhaps always will be.

From another point of view, and one completely compatible with the first, gravitation is simply the effect of warped space. This warping affects every property of space including the passage of light. Thus starlight passing near our sun should follow a curved trajectory, and this phenomenon is observed. The planets in their orbits are pursuing natural courses in the warped channels produced by the masses of sun and planets. Unfortunately, there seems little possibility that these spheres do any singing on their way.

ELECTROMAGNETISM

Most of the forces that concern humans in this world are electromagnetic. All of the ordinary chemical and biological effects are due to the interaction of electric charges and the fields they produce. These are just the atomic and molecular binding forces. The effects of electromagnetism include the radiant energy spectrum all the way from the radio wave whistlers with wavelengths of thousands of miles to gamma rays which can be used to probe the structure of the nucleon.

We use the combined term *electromagnetism* because, of course, electricity and magnetism are both part of the same phenomenon, a force more complicated,

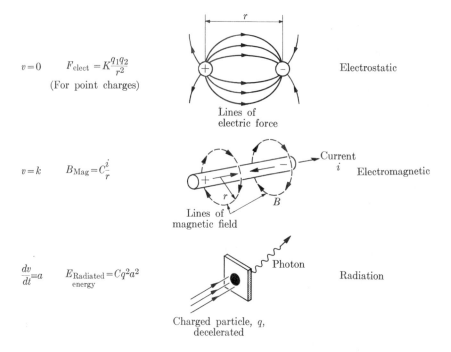

$$v = 0 \qquad F_{\text{elect}} = K\frac{q_1 q_2}{r^2}$$
(For point charges)

Lines of
electric force

Electrostatic

$$v = k \qquad B_{\text{Mag}} = C\frac{i}{r}$$

Current
i
Electromagnetic

B

Lines of
magnetic field

$$\frac{dv}{dt} \equiv a \qquad E_{\text{Radiated}} = Cq^2 a^2$$
energy

Photon

Radiation

Charged particle, q,
decelerated

FIG. 28. Dependence of electromagnetic fields on velocity of source charge.

however, than gravity. Not only are there negative charges as well as positive, but the interaction depends on the relative velocity of the charges (Fig. 28). If the charges are at rest with respect to each other and us, we describe the effect as *electrostatic*. If the relative motion is one of constant velocity, the action can be partially described in terms of a magnetic field. If a charge is accelerated, an observer can detect radiant electromagnetic energy leaving the system.

The electrostatic case is the simplest and appears the most familiar. The appropriate law for the interaction of point charges bears the name of Coulomb:

$$F = k\frac{q_1 q_2}{r^2} \, .$$

The constant k depends on the nature of the space between the charges and also depends on the units chosen for the other variables. In our standard meter-kilogram-second system, the unit of charge, q, is the coulomb. This is a familiar unit in electricity since a current of one ampere is the passage of one coulomb of charge per second. With the separation r measured in meters, and the force F in newtons, k has the value, for free space, of 9×10^9 n·m²/coul². If the medium between the charges is not empty space, a more complicated situation arises. There are two types of charges, positive and negative, and the internal distribution of the charges in matter can be disturbed by an outside electric field. These polarization effects act as a shield for the electric forces. There is no equivalent phenomenon in gravity.

The coulomb is an enormous amount of isolated charge. One coulomb of positive charge on a conductor one meter away from a conductor containing a negative coulomb would produce a force of attraction of 9×10^9 newtons. In more familiar terms, since a kilogram weighs about 10 newtons, this is equal to the weight of about 10^9 kg or 2.2×10^9 lb or about one million tons. Of course, one coulomb could not be isolated like that; the voltage produced would be flashing lightning bolts long before the coulomb was assembled. In spite of this, the lowly flashlight battery can produce currents of one or two coulombs per second for an hour or more. The explanation, of course, is that the negative charges are flowing past equal amounts of positive charge and are not being isolated (Fig. 29).

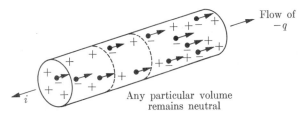

FIG. 29. Current flow does not require charge separation.

Coulomb's law has most of the characteristics of Newton's gravitational formula. Both are correct for isolated point sources, or spheres. The force is in the direction of the connecting line but, in the electrical case, can be attractive or repulsive since either q_1 or q_2 may be positive or negative. We shall use our arbitrary standard situation to compute the relative strength of the interaction. Two protons, 10^{-15} meter apart, will be repelled by a force

$$F = k \frac{q_1 q_2}{r^2} = 9 \times 10^9 \frac{(1.6 \times 10^{-19})^2}{(10^{-15})^2} \approx 30 \text{ newtons.}$$

This is 10^{35} times as great as the gravitational attraction caused by this mass. The energy released by the complete separation of these two protons would be about 3×10^{-14} joule or 2×10^5 ev. So the electric force between particles is enormous compared with the gravitational attraction, but is only about 1% of the nuclear binding.

The simple formula of electrostatics is not sufficient if the particles are moving. An observer would detect as a charge passed by, not only an electric field, but also a magnetic field. The strength of this new field is proportional to the velocity and to the magnitude of the charge. Furthermore the strength is not directed toward the charge, but is at right angles to that direction and to the velocity. Since in most cases of interest there is relative motion between particles, the whole phenomenon of electromagnetism must be taken into account.

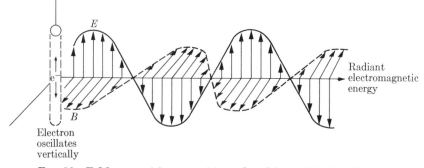

Fig. 30. E-M waves (along x-axis) produced by oscillating charge.

Ordinary magnetism, for instance, can be explained as an effect of the behavior of moving electrons in the atoms or molecules.

The electric and magnetic aspects of the fields which are set up by moving charges involve no loss of energy from the source. The electron or proton does not have a weaker charge when it is influencing distant objects. However, whenever a charge is accelerated, notice of this effect radiates out in the form of an electric and magnetic pulse which represents energy that does not return to the source. The lost radiant energy comes from the agent which accelerates the charge.

This pulse is called a photon and travels at a constant speed of 3×10^8 m/sec in free space. If the source charge is accelerating in an oscillating fashion, as shown in Fig. 30, the propagated signal will consist of successive waves of electric and magnetic fields. In a radio antenna the electrons may vibrate up and down at a rate of 1 million times per second. The frequency of the radiated fields will be the same, and since wavelength times frequency equals velocity, $\lambda \times \nu = c$ (velocity of light),

$$\lambda \times 10^6 \text{ cycles/sec} = 3 \times 10^8 \text{ m/sec}$$

and

$$\lambda = 300 \text{ meters.}$$

Radio waves are very long. On the other hand, when an electron jumps to a more stable atomic position and gives up its energy of excitation, its wavelength in the visible region, is about 5×10^{-7} meter. This corresponds to a frequency of

$$\nu \times \lambda = c$$
$$\nu \times 5 \times 10^{-7} \text{ meter} = 3 \times 10^8 \text{ m/sec}$$
$$\nu = 6 \times 10^{14} \text{ cycles/sec.}$$

In the first case it makes sense to picture the electrons actually oscillating up and down a wire at a rate of one megacycle. The wave nature of the radiation is of primary importance and it takes a vivid imagination to think of radio "photons." In the optical region, the circumstances are not so clear. Certainly it is meaningless to picture the atomic electron oscillating at 6×10^{14} cycles/sec on its way down to a stable orbit. The energy is emitted in a pulse, a photon. On the other hand, since this wavelength is comparable in size to many objects accessible to humans—fine scratches, pin holes, sharp edges—it is fairly easy to see the interference phenomena best described in terms of waves.

A million volt x-ray or γ-ray (artificial distinctions used to name photons from atomic or nuclear processes) will have a frequency of 3×10^{20} cycles/sec. The wave nature is unimportant for most purposes; a γ-ray usually acts like a particle.

The energy of any photon is given by $E = h\nu$, where h is Planck's constant. For the three cases considered, the energy involved in a single photon is

Radio	Optical	X-ray
$\nu = 10^6$ cycles/sec	$\nu = 6 \times 10^{14}$	$\nu = 3 \times 10^{20}$
$E \approx 6 \times 10^{-34} \times 10^6$	$E \approx 6 \times 10^{-34} \times 6 \times 10^{14}$	$E \approx 6 \times 10^{-34} \times 3 \times 10^{20}$
$\approx 6 \times 10^{-28}$ joule	$\approx 4 \times 10^{-19}$ joule	$\approx 1.8 \times 10^{-13}$ joule
$\approx 4 \times 10^{-9}$ ev	≈ 3 ev	≈ 1 Mev

In all cases the photons, traveling at the speed of light, act as the agents of the electromagnetic field. The model used for mathematical descriptions of interacting particles is one where photons are emitted and reabsorbed by a charge thus establishing the electromagnetic field. So long as the source charge is not disturbed, these photons are not lost. Interaction between two particles consists of an exchange of these photons. Acceleration of a charge shakes photons loose so that they do not return, or in other words, a new field pattern has been established and the lead messengers of the change travel on forever.

STRONG NUCLEAR FORCE

Even with the simple atom of protons, neutrons, and electrons, it is clear enough that there must be a special force associated with the nucleus. The electrostatic force of repulsion of the protons is large and must be overcome by some strong attraction. As we have seen, gravity is far too weak to supply the binding and need not even be considered for particle reactions. Many qualitative facts about the nuclear force were discovered simply by observing the existence and stability of various atoms. Other details have been added by "atom" smashing experiments where probe particles have been scattered off nuclei, sometimes transmuting them to other kinds.

The strong nuclear force is independent of the electric charge. There is the same force between proton-proton, proton-neutron, and neutron-neutron. In fact, as far as this interaction is concerned, the proton and neutron are one and the same thing but in different electric charge states, even as two magnets might be in different energy states if a magnetic field were turned on.

This force cannot easily be described in terms of a strength-distance relationship. It certainly does not follow an inverse square behavior but, instead, is a short-range force. If two nucleons are touching, they are strongly attracted. When they are separated, the force falls to zero. It is like the behavior of scotch tape, but for quite different reasons! The range of effective force is about 1.3×10^{-15} meter, which, by no accident, defines the radius of the nucleon.

The nuclear force does depend, however, on the orientation of the nucleons. They have spin $\frac{1}{2}\hbar$ each and so, being fermions, are subject to the saturation rules of the Pauli exclusion principle. In a proton scattering experiment, the proton-proton deflection pattern will be different from the proton-neutron pattern partly because certain close arrangements of the two protons with their spins in the same direction are forbidden while the proton-neutron combination is not subject to this restriction.

The spin orientation requirements have great effect on the stability of nuclei. We do not find stable nuclei consisting of many neutrons and only a few protons because this is not so compact an arrangement as one with about equal numbers of protons and neutrons. The most stable subgrouping consists of two protons and two neutrons (Fig. 31). As the diagram shows, the two spins of the same mode of nucleon can be in opposite directions, satis-

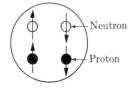

FIG. 31. Nucleon spins in helium.

fying the exclusion principle. If another nucleon is added to the group, it must be in a higher energy state, much as happens to an extra electron in atomic orbits. A nucleus containing too many neutrons would be in a higher energy state than one with matching protons. Whenever an object can fall from a higher energy state to a low it will do so. In the case of too many neutrons, the unstable nucleus would change itself to a more stable form by converting one or more neutrons to protons, emitting electrons (β-rays) to account for the change in electric charge. The same thing happens, with the emission of positrons, if a nucleus is created with too many protons. Here there is the additional instability presented by the electrostatic repulsion of the extra positive charge. Such transformations occur naturally in radioactive materials or can be induced by the artificial creation of unstable nuclei in reactors or accelerators. The greater the asymmetry in proton-neutron number, the faster will be the decay and the more energetic the emitted β-particle.

There are some exceptions to these general considerations, of course. Nuclei can sustain an imbalance of two in the number of extra protons and neutrons and still be stable. For instance, there are three stable isotopes of oxygen: $_8O^{16}$, $_8O^{17}$, $_8O^{18}$. If the second extra neutron in $_8O^{18}$ were to change to a proton, leaving fluorine $_9F^{18}$, the resulting nucleus would be less stable than the original. In fact, $_9F^{18}$ is radioactive and decays to $_8O^{18}$. The pairing arrangement is responsible for this. There is greater stability in pairing the same particles with opposite spin.

There is another revealing characteristic of the table of stable isotopes. As the nuclei get heavier, they evidently are more stable if they do have more neutrons than protons (Fig. 32). The heaviest stable nucleus is one of lead,

$_{82}Pb^{208}$. ($_{83}Bi^{209}$ may or may not be stable. If not, its half life is about 10^{17} years.) This has 82 protons and 126 neutrons. What happened to our rule? To be sure, this nucleus must be on the edge of instability because all the heavier nuclei are radioactive, and the ones above uranium are so unstable that they do not even exist naturally. The disturbing factor which changes our rule is the electrostatic repulsion of the protons.

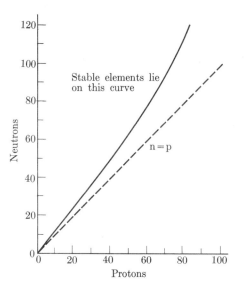

FIG. 32. Nuclear stability for large nuclei requires neutron surplus.

As more and more nucleons are assembled, the energy of repulsion goes up as the square of the number of protons, $Z(Z - 1)$. Each proton pushes on all the others, with a force which is almost the same whether the other proton is on one side of the nucleus or on the other. On the other hand, the nuclear binding is short range and is effective only between adjacent neighbors. The total energy of nuclear binding thus increases only as the first power of the number of nucleons, or the atomic weight, A. A slight correction must also be made for the edge effects. A nucleon on the outside is not held so tightly as one in the center. This effect helps to make the nuclei in the middle of the table (iron, copper, etc.) the most stable. While the dissociation effect of the positive charge increases with increasing atomic number, the volume-to-surface ratio also increases, and this provides greater binding. In other words, the light nuclei have too much surface and so not enough nuclear binding; the heavy nuclei have too much electrostatic repulsion; the medium nuclei strike the most stable compromise (Fig. 33).

For some purposes it is useful to picture the nuclear force as arising from a field, described in a fashion similar to that of the gravitational or electromagnetic field. Figure 34 shows the nucleus as a potential well, having a depth corresponding to the strength of the binding and a width associated with the range. At the boundaries a *charged* particle would meet an electrostatic barrier caused

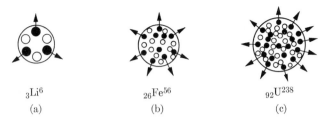

$_3\text{Li}^6$ $_{26}\text{Fe}^{56}$ $_{92}\text{U}^{238}$

(a)   (b)   (c)

Fig. 33. Considerations that account for maximum stability of nuclei in the middle of the periodic table. (a) There is a large surface area compared with the volume. Here there is small electrostatic repulsion. (b) There is a smaller proportion of exposed nucleons on the surface. The electrostatic repulsion is still not too great. (c) The high ratio of volume to area gives strong nuclear binding to many nucleons, but the total electrostatic effect makes the system unstable.

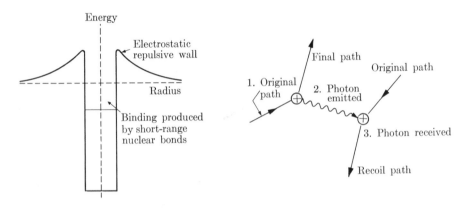

Fig. 34. Potential wall and well seen by charged particle in presence of nucleus.

Fig. 35. Electromagnetic interaction through exchange of photon agents.

by the positive protons. A neutron would *not* see this feature, but a bombarding proton must possess enough energy to clear the obstacle if it is to penetrate the nucleus. Thus, in general, nuclear disintegrations occur only with charged particle probes of energy over 1 Mev. The height of the barrier depends, of course, on the amount of charge inside.

Another model of the nuclear force pictures the nucleons emitting and receiving agents or messengers. There is good precedent for such a model. One way to picture electromagnetic interactions is to consider the exchange of agents, in this case photons, between charged particles (Fig. 35). The field is considered to exist in the region in which the photons are sent out and received. Since these photons are not lost to the system, there is no energy loss, unless the source is accelerated. The electric forces are the result of the interaction of these agents with the charges. The illustration in Fig. 35 shows just one such interaction and necessarily presents it in terms of a collision with drastic recoil. Actually, each charged particle should be considered to be surrounded by a large number of photons which it has emitted and will soon reabsorb. They are the "field." The interaction between two particles is composed of an enormous number of emissions, recoils, and absorptions, one example of which is shown in Fig. 35. Since in most cases the photons have very low energy, it is really not appropriate to picture them localized in space as shown in the diagram. It is the old duality problem again. At these energies, the probability of finding the photon is best described in terms of waves. Nevertheless, this model is the basis for successful calculations of electromagnetic interactions.

The Japanese physicist, Yukawa, proposed in 1935 that an analogous theory would be useful to explain nuclear forces. The agents of the force could not, of course, be photons; photons transmit electromagnetic effects. Since the force is short range, the messengers must have mass, and the amount can be roughly calculated from Heisenberg's uncertainty principle. If a nucleon emits a particle with mass, its own mass-energy must be lower. Yet we always observe nucleons with the same rest mass. While mass-energy must be conserved, still there are limits to how accurately it can be measured at a particular time and thus, according to our philosophy, there are limits to the intrinsic energy-time definiteness. If we require a nucleon to send out a massive particle to make contact across the nuclear force range, for how long a time is there an uncertainty in the energy? It must roughly be the time it takes the particle, traveling as fast as it can go, the speed of light, to go 1.3×10^{-15} meter.

$$\Delta t = \frac{1.3 \times 10^{-15} \text{ meter}}{3 \times 10^8 \text{ m/sec}} \approx 4 \times 10^{-24} \text{ sec.}$$

The uncertainty relationship requires

$$\Delta E \times \Delta t \geq \hbar \approx 1 \times 10^{-34},$$
$$\Delta E \approx 2 \times 10^{-11} \text{ joule,}$$
$$\approx 10^8 \text{ ev.}$$

This energy, 100 Mev, is about two hundred times that of the rest mass energy of the electron. Therefore, the agent of the nuclear force could have a mass about 200 times that of the electron and could be tossed back and forth between nucleons without noticeably violating energy-mass conservation.

Such a particle was promptly discovered in the cosmic radiation. Unfortunately, it was observed at sea level and under Lake Cayuga as well as on mountain tops. This was supposed to be the nuclear glue, but it seemed to be able to penetrate the whole atmosphere without interacting with matter. Instead, it should have suffered a nuclear collision in air every kilometer or so. The paradox was not resolved until after World War II. Then the trails of high-energy particle collisions of cosmic rays were recorded in photographic plates which had been flown near the top of the atmosphere. The particles that came out of these collisions were not the sea level cosmic ray particles, but were heavier. These heavier particles do interact strongly with matter and are true mesons. After a brief existence they decay into slightly lighter particles which then penetrate deeply, being slowed down only by the energy loss caused by their electric charge effects.

These nuclear glue mesons were given the name π (pi) and are often called pions. Since there has to be equal chance of interaction between proton-proton, proton-neutron, and neutron-neutron, the pions must exist electrically positive, negative, and neutral. Qualitatively, the model provides a description of forces within nuclei and between individual nucleons, but quantitatively there is still no good theory. Many other mesons are now known: κ, η, and particles which lead an existence even more transitory than these. The dividing line between nucleon source and meson agent is not so clear, as we shall see in the last section.

WEAK INTERACTION

Most of the particles listed on the chart have very short half lives. The hyperons decay down into nucleons and mesons in times of about 10^{-10} sec; the pions decay into muons in 10^{-8} sec; and the muons collapse to electrons in 10^{-6} sec. But these times are short only by our human standards, and hardly that any more. Several thousand electronic engineers and physicists in this world routinely measure times in the range of a millionth of a second. When you are used to counting time in units of nanoseconds (10^{-9}), a microsecond seems long enough to go down to the corner store and back. On the nuclear scale, these lifetimes are enormous. A suitable unit of nuclear time is the time taken for light to cross a nucleon diameter, 10^{-23} sec. From this viewpoint, one must ask, "What makes an unstable particle last for such an eternity?"

The strong interactions all take place in times of about 10^{-23} sec. During this short interval pions and kaons are emitted and absorbed and the participants go on their way. Yet some of the resulting particles, although energetically unstable, suffer no decay until a time 10^{13} greater has come and gone (Fig. 36). There is the same problem in β decay of radioactive nuclei. Here the situation is more complicated because of the collective motions of all the nucleons in the nucleus and the extreme sensitivity of the decay to the amount of energy available. Decay times of seconds can occur. Nevertheless, these

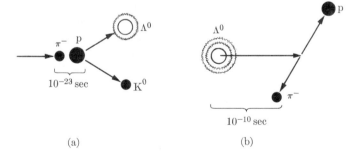

(a)   (b)

FIG. 36. Strange stability of strange particles. (a) Production in nuclear times. (b) Decay into original particles takes 10^{13} times longer.

nuclear and nucleon structure effects are not sufficient to account for the long periods of pseudostability. If the strong, nuclear interactions are involved, and a reaction is suitable energetically and dynamically (i.e., if momentum and angular momentum can be conserved), then the reaction should take place in nuclear times. If only the electromagnetic force is involved, the time of reaction should be longer than the nuclear time by a factor of 100 or so since the interaction is weaker. Therefore, it must be that if a reaction does not occur in these times either the participants are not subject to these two forces or else there is some new conservation law or prohibition which forbids the decay. Since most of the particles involved are subject to either the nuclear force or have electric charge or both, there must be some rule which stops the process. But since eventually the decays do happen, there must therefore be a fourth type of interaction which is not subject to the restrictions. The existence of such a force was proposed by Fermi in the early 1930's to explain β decay, but we still know very little about it. Considering the relatively long time that particles need to respond to it, it must be very weak compared with the strong nuclear force. The relative strength is about 10^{-13}, and for lack of any other name, it is called simply, the Weak Interaction.

We would like to place responsibility on the Weak Interaction for decays as dissimilar as

$$n \rightarrow p + e^- + \bar{\nu}_e \quad \text{with} \quad t_{1/2} = 700 \text{ sec and no change in strangeness}$$

$$\Lambda^0 \rightarrow \pi^- + p \quad \text{with} \quad t_{1/2} = 1.7 \times 10^{-10} \text{ sec and strangeness change } +1$$

Perhaps there are several types of interaction responsible, but it would be more satisfying if only one were sufficient.

In every case such a decay can be described as an interaction among four fermions. For example, consider the reactions which do not involve a change of strangeness and yet which must be due to the Weak Interaction. The neutron decay is the prototype of all the β decays,

$$n \rightarrow p + e^- + \bar{\nu}_e.$$

The nature of such an "equation" is that the reaction can go in either direction so long as energy is conserved, and that any participant can be replaced on the opposite side by its antiparticle. For instance,

$$p \rightarrow n + e^+ + \nu_e.$$

This would be the prototype for positron decay. Of course, an isolated proton will not decay like this, because it is lighter than the neutron and so there is not sufficient energy for the reaction. Another variation of this four-fermion interaction is the proton capture of an antineutrino, which has been observed and will be discussed in Section 7,

$$\bar{\nu}_e + p \rightarrow n + e^+.$$

The muon decay is another example of the four-fermion interaction,

$$\mu^- \rightarrow e^- + \nu_\mu + \bar{\nu}_e.$$

Note here that we differentiate between neutrinos associated with muons (ν_μ) and neutrinos associated with electrons (ν_e). The experimental evidence for this distinction is described in Section 7.

So far we have written equations for the coupling of nucleons, electrons, and neutrinos, and for the coupling of muons, electrons, and neutrinos. To complete the arrangement, there is a coupling among muons, nucleons, and neutrinos, thus,

$$\mu^- + p \rightarrow n + \nu_\mu.$$

The reaction rates of all these combinations are consistent with a theory which ascribes the same strength to the three different types, the so-called Universal Fermi Interaction. There are, however, other types of weak interactions which require couplings between other pairs of fermions.

Consider the weak decay,

$$\underset{S=-1}{\Lambda^0} \rightarrow \underset{S=0}{\pi^-} + \underset{S=0}{p} .$$

There is no neutrino involved here, strangeness changes by $+1$, and there are apparently only two fermions involved! Nevertheless, there is a way in which four fermions can be involved and the mechanism is typical of a whole class of reactions. The decay takes place through a *virtual* stage.

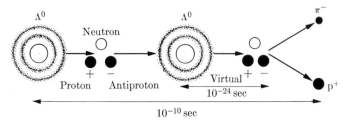

Fig. 37. Weak Interaction decay of Λ^0 by way of virtual dissociation into neutron and proton-antiproton pair.

Virtual reactions must be considered because of the Heisenberg Uncertainty Law: Δ Energy $\times \Delta$ time $\geq \hbar$. During a short interval of time, Δt, the energy may be uncertain by ΔE. During a time of 10^{-24} sec, the uncertainty in energy is about 1 Bev. The Λ^0, for example, could momentarily "decay" thus (Fig. 37),

$$\Lambda^0 \rightarrow \bar{p}^- + n^0 + p^+.$$

The extra energy needed for the creation of the proton-antiproton pair is about 2 Bev. Of course, the reaction cannot stay that way long enough for the particles to be observed by ordinary detection methods. Presumably, though, this reaction plus many others even more complicated might be going on. If so, there is a chance that during the reaction time the nucleon-antinucleon pair might annihilate each other, turning into particles with which they are strongly associated, pions, for instance. Even though the virtual reaction lasts a very short time, the strong nuclear reactions take only 10^{-23} sec to act. Of course, the final products of this two-step process must satisfy all the necessary conservation laws:

$$\Lambda^0 \rightarrow (\overline{p} + n + p) \rightarrow \pi^- + p.$$
$$\text{virtual}$$

In the first virtual step, four fermions are involved. In the next stage, the strong nuclear forces come into play. Unfortunately, we do not know whether or not the strength of the coupling among these fermions is the same as that among the neutrino-electron and proton-neutron, etc. Furthermore, there is no good way to calculate the details of the second step, since that involves the strong interaction, which also has an incomplete theory.

It might seem as if the introduction of the virtual process is like inventing angels to dance on pin heads. However, the necessity of considering such intermediate steps follows logically from the Uncertainty Principle. Furthermore, its use in the theory of electromagnetism leads to completely correct predictions. In the case of the weak interactions, the rough calculations that are possible yield qualitative explanations of many of the observed phenomena.

So far we have described the Weak Interaction as some sort of coupling between two pairs of fermions. It is not clear that only one such coupling is involved: each pair may have its own peculiar strength or "charge." There is also the problem as to whether or not an agent of this force can be described. There is the graviton for gravity, photon for electromagnetism, and mesons for the strong nuclear force. If there is a similar agent for the Weak Interaction, it would also be a boson and would probably have a mass above 800 Mev. It is referred to as the Intermediate Charged Vector Boson, and is given the symbol W. Presumably, its half life against decay into electron-neutrino or muon-neutrino would be less than 10^{-17} sec.

During the summer of 1963 a major attempt was made to detect such a particle in high-energy neutrino experiments at the European Center for Nuclear Research at Geneva. A high-energy neutrino (from a pi-meson decay and therefore, ν_μ) colliding with a proton might produce a muon and the intermediate boson, leaving behind the proton. Immediately the intermediate boson would decay into a positron and neutrino.

$$\nu_\mu + p \rightarrow p + W^+_{\text{(intermediate boson)}} + \mu^-$$
$$\qquad\qquad\qquad \hookrightarrow e^+ + \nu_e$$

It is unlikely that the effect has been detected. The data obtained so far indicates that if the W exists, its mass must be greater than that of the nucleon.

Needless to say, such a confusing situation is a sheer delight to those pouncing on the field. In a few years these problems will probably be solved, only to reveal more subtle and complicated questions that we do not now realize exist.

Not all particles are subject to all four types of force. The photons and neutrinos have no mass and yet photons, at least, must follow the warped space produced by other mass. They are, therefore, from another point of view, attracted by gravity. Photons are agents of the electromagnetic force, and yet are not influenced by electromagnetic fields. Neutrinos have no electromagnetic interaction at all. The electron, the muon, the neutrinos, and the photons do not seem to be subject to the strong nuclear forces. Indeed, the neutrinos are apparently subject only to the weak interactions and, presumably, the far weaker gravitational force. There are laws governing the behavior of particles under the influence of these forces, and not all laws apply to all forces. In the next chapter we consider the question of which properties are changed and which are conserved in the four types of interactions.

LIST OF PLATES

ACKNOWLEDGMENTS

Plate II is reproduced through the courtesy of Dr. Lester Germer;

Plate IV through the courtesy of the "Cambridge Bubble Chamber Group," Brown University, Harvard University, M.I.T., Brandeis;

Plate IX through the courtesy of Professor Leon Lederman, Columbia University;

Plate XI through the courtesy of Professor C. D. Anderson, California Institute of Technology;

Plate XIII through the courtesy of Professor Robert K. Adair, Yale University.

All other plates are reproduced through the courtesy of the Brookhaven National Laboratory, Upton, New York.

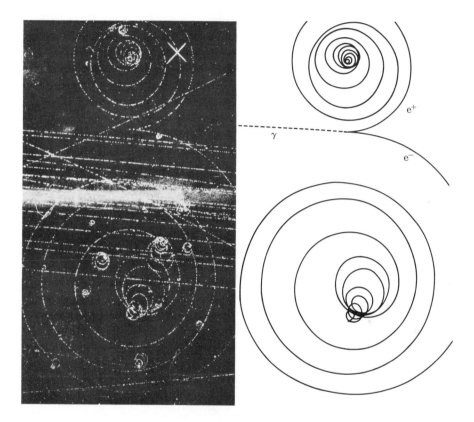

PLATE I. Electron pair creation.

PLATE II.   Electron diffraction.

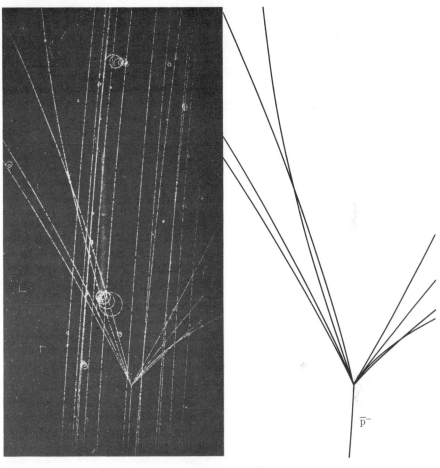

$$\overline{p}^- + p^+ \longrightarrow 4\pi^+ + 4\pi^- + x\pi^0$$

PLATE III.   Antiproton annihilation.

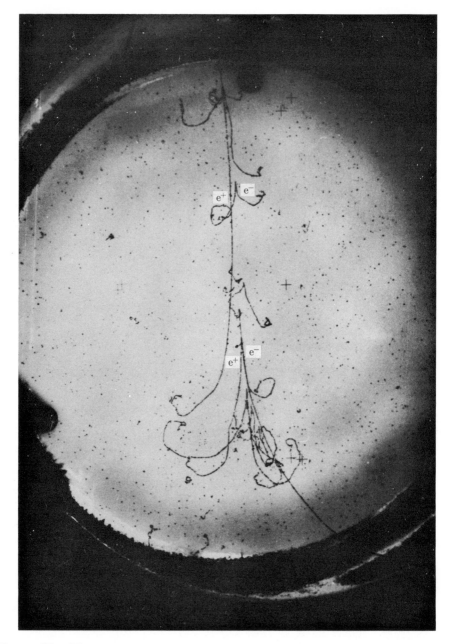

PLATE IV. Electron-gamma shower formation. An electron with momentum of 1 *Bev/c* (and therefore energy of $\sim$1 Bev) entered a methyl iodide propane bubble chamber, initiating a shower of gammas and pair electrons. The entire development can be seen because of the high density and high Z of the medium.

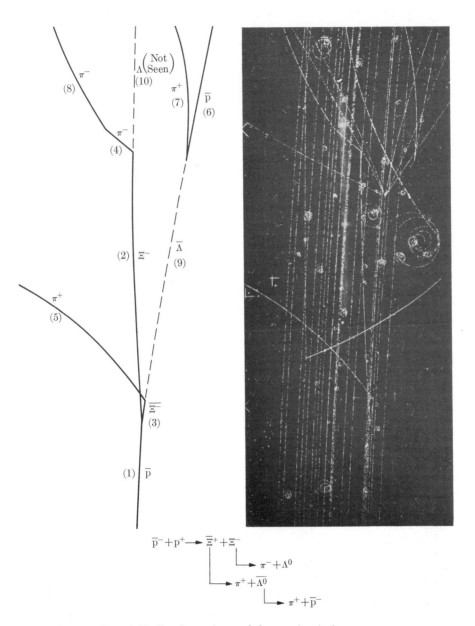

PLATE V. Dual creation and destruction in baryons.

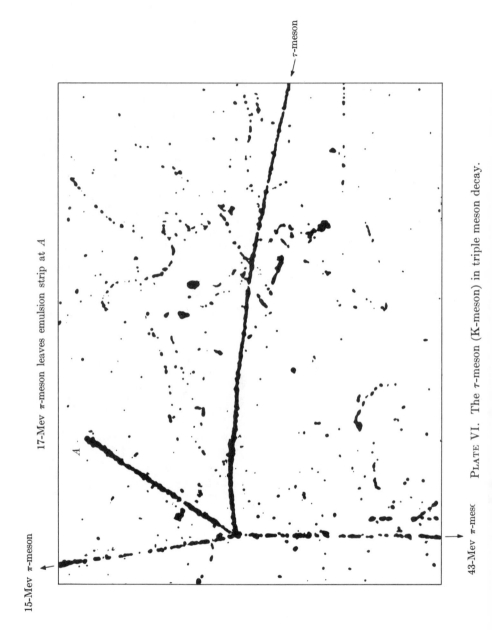

17-Mev π-meson leaves emulsion strip at A

15-Mev π-meson

τ-meson

43-Mev π-meson

PLATE VI.   The τ-meson (K-meson) in triple meson decay.

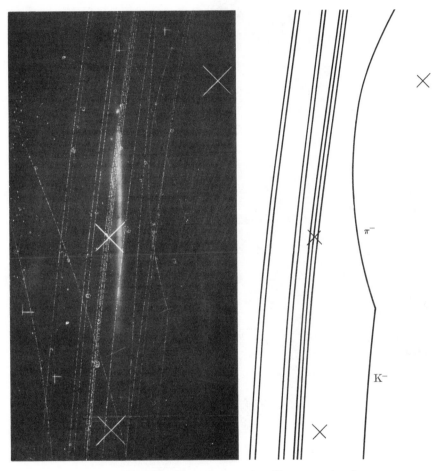

PLATE VII. K⁻ decay by θ-mode. $K^- \to \pi^- + \pi^0$.

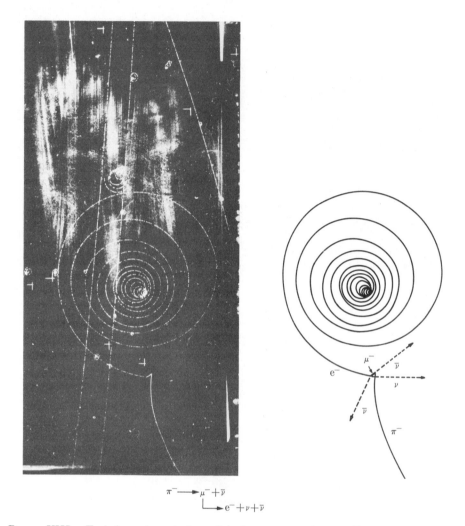

$$\pi^- \longrightarrow \mu^- + \bar{\nu}$$
$$ \mkern-18mu \raisebox{0pt}{$\llcorner$}\!\!\longrightarrow e^- + \nu + \bar{\nu}$$

PLATE VIII. Emission of neutral particle in π-meson decay. Decay sequence of π meson. Note that for momentum conservation, neutral particles must be emitted in π and μ decay.

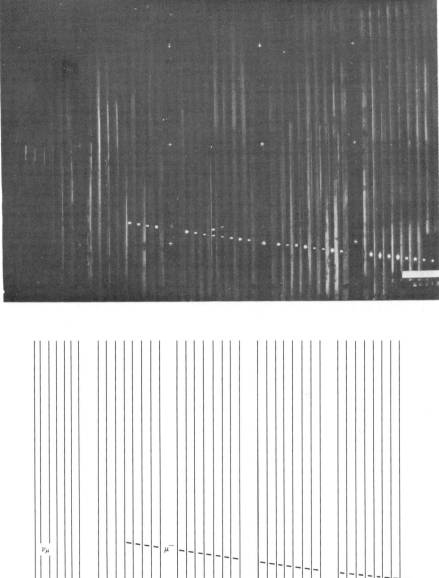

PLATE IX.   One of the group of pictures showing μ production from ν_μ, but never e production.   Apparently, ν_μ is different from ν_e.

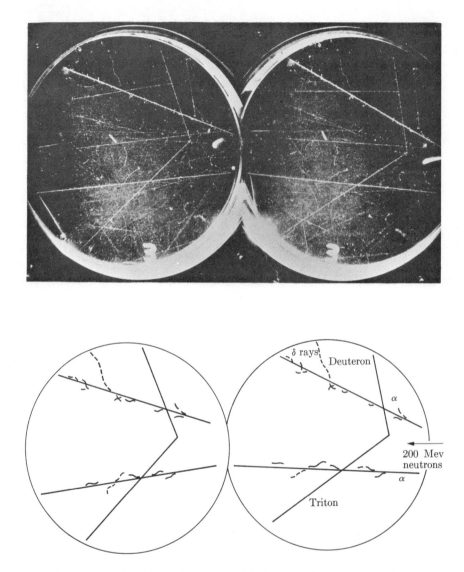

PLATE X. Stereoscopic picture of elastic and inelastic collisions of 200 Mev neutrons with helium in cloud chamber.   One helium nucleus was split into a deuteron and triton.   Two others were knocked forward with high energy.   Their trails are thick because of their double charge.   Notice the δ-ray electrons struck by the passing α with sufficient energy to allow them to form tracks of their own.

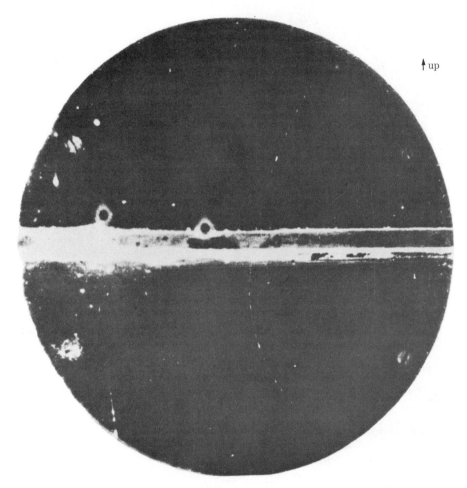

↑ up

PLATE XI. The first definite picture of a positron track. The track had curvature appropriate for positive particle, assuming it was coming from top to bottom. Greater curvature in bottom section indicates lower energy. Therefore particle must have come from top and lost energy going through plate.

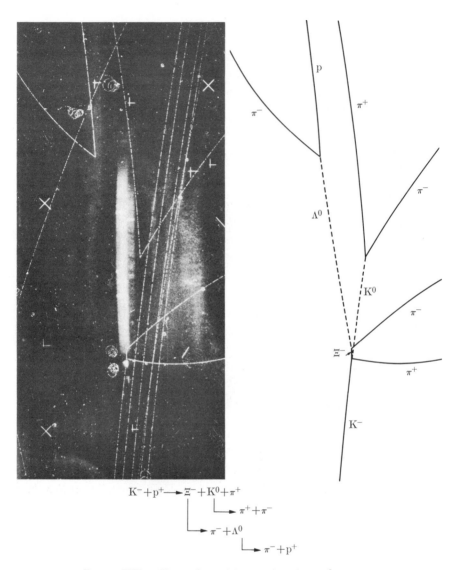

$$K^- + p^+ \longrightarrow \Xi^- + K^0 + \pi^+$$
$$ \llcorner\rightarrow \pi^+ + \pi^-$$
$$ \llcorner\rightarrow \pi^- + \Lambda^0$$
$$ \llcorner\rightarrow \pi^- + p^+$$

PLATE XII.   Charged particles produced in K^0 decay.

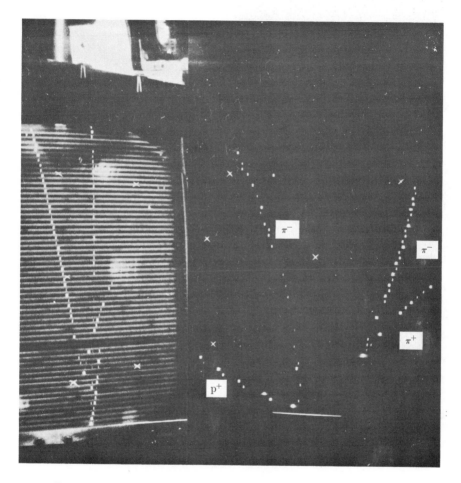

PLATE XIII. Stereoscopic views of Λ^0-K^0 decay in spark chamber.

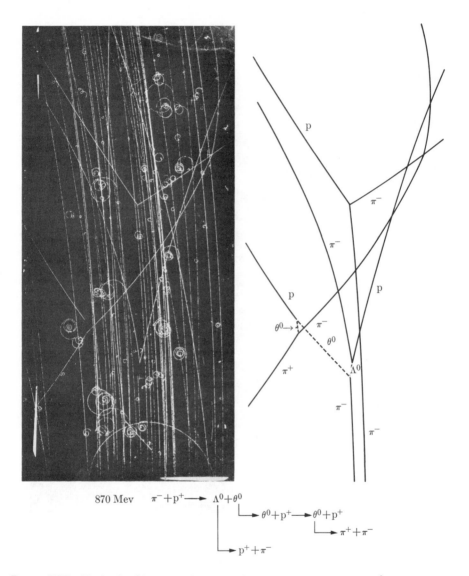

870 Mev $\pi^- + p^+ \longrightarrow \Lambda^0 + \theta^0$
$\qquad\qquad\qquad\qquad\quad \hookrightarrow \theta^0 + p^+ \longrightarrow \theta^0 + p^+$
$\qquad\qquad\qquad\qquad\qquad\qquad\qquad\qquad \hookrightarrow \pi^+ + \pi^-$
$\qquad\qquad\qquad\qquad\quad \hookrightarrow p^+ + \pi^-$

PLATE XIV. Notice in this unusual picture the elastic collision of the θ^0 with a proton in the hydrogen bubble chamber.

Section 6.   The Conservation Laws

We learn about anything in this world only through its interactions with other things. A passive, isolated object is unknowable. Even to see something we must have a scattering or reflection of photons from the object to our eyes, where in turn a whole sequence of other interactions begins. The most obvious feature of any interaction is that the participants change. They either change their motion or perhaps their very nature. But the most useful characteristic is that certain qualities do not change. They are conserved.

Some of these conservation laws are familiar from classical science. Most of them were proposed or discovered only within the last three hundred years. To illustrate the nature of these laws with a small quibble, let us claim that it is not quite correct to think of them as immutable laws which man has finally stumbled upon. A more accurate statement of the situation is that it has been found possible to define certain quantities associated with systems in such a way that these quantities do not change. In other words, men have gone to some trouble to *define* such qualities as energy and momentum in such a way that they are usually constant under the right conditions. For example, everyone knows these days that heat is just one form of energy, although this easy knowledge was not so obvious up to about one hundred years ago. In elementary physics laboratories, a favorite experiment is to measure the value of the *mechanical equivalent* of heat, usually by letting a mechanical system stir and so heat up some water. From one viewpoint, the experiment demonstrates the conservation of energy. Mechanical energy disappears; the temperature of the substance rises. From another viewpoint, we save the energy conservation law by defining a new form of energy—heat—and the experiment merely yields the numerical value of our *defined* form of energy. A great many forms of energy have been thus discovered and/or defined. The test of such definitions, of course, is their consistency in simplifying the description of the complicated events we observe. When we find such widespread consistency, we are justified in thinking that our laws reflect a real attribute of the universe itself.

CONSERVATION OF MASS-ENERGY

One of the forms of energy is mass. In chemical reactions, the amount of energy exchanged is usually so small that measurement of the change in mass is just beyond the accuracy of present techniques. When a molecule of hydrogen is burned with oxygen, chemical energy of 2.5 ev is released. The energy from a mole of the resulting water molecules would be 1.5×10^{24} ev, or 2.5×10^5 joules. The mass which has disappeared to provide this energy can be found from the Einstein relation

$$E = m_0 c^2,$$

$$10^5 \text{ joules} = m_{\mathrm{kg}} \times (3 \times 10^8 \text{ m/sec})^2 \approx m_{\mathrm{kg}} 10^{17}, \qquad m_0 \approx 10^{-12} \text{ kg}.$$

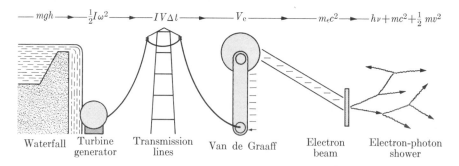

$$-mgh \longrightarrow -\tfrac{1}{2}I\omega^2 \longrightarrow IV\Delta t \longrightarrow V_e \longrightarrow m_e c^2 \longrightarrow h\nu + mc^2 + \tfrac{1}{2} mv^2$$

Waterfall   Turbine   Transmission   Van de Graaff   Electron   Electron-photon
             generator   lines   beam   shower

FIG. 38. Energy conservation. The test of the law and its definitions is the consistency with which the enormous number of phenomena is described.

The mole of water molecules has a mass of 18 grams, but the loss of mass is only 10^{-9} gm. To measure this would require weighing techniques sensitive to one part in 10 billion. In nuclear interactions, however, individual energy transfers are over a million times greater. The fission of $_{92}U^{235}$ provides about 200 Mev, or almost one Mev per nucleon. Since each nucleon has a mass of about one Bev, there is an easily measured mass loss of one-tenth percent.

With kinetic energy and the various forms of potential energy, including mass, properly defined, all natural phenomena can be consistently described as satisfying the law of conservation of energy. The truthfulness of the law is a matter of the consistency of our definitions. It is an amazing intellectual triumph that so few hypotheses are able to satisfy so many diverse events.

Consider the chain of reactions involved in the acceleration of an electron in a Van de Graaff machine (Fig. 38). Mechanical energy, supplied by an electric motor, which in turn was supplied by falling water or burning coal, transports electrons to the high voltage region on a moving belt. There, each electron may have an electric potential energy of three million electron volts. The electron is accelerated down a vacuum tube toward ground where it is at zero electric potential, but it now has kinetic energy and extra mass equal to 3 Mev. Since the electron rest mass energy is $\tfrac{1}{2}$ Mev, its total mass-energy is $3\tfrac{1}{2}$ Mev; it is traveling at about 98% of the speed of light and has a mass seven times normal. If it passes close to a heavy nucleus in a target its path will be radically altered. Since an accelerated charge emits electromagnetic radiation, a high energy photon (γ-ray or x-ray) will be created. The deflected electron and x-ray will continue, each producing slightly different effects. The electron will excite and ionize atoms in its path. The excited atoms will settle back to normal emitting electromagnetic radiation (photons of ultraviolet or visible or infrared) or vibrating and thus heating up the whole molecular structure. The x-ray may strike electrons in the material, knocking them forward as in billiard-ball collisions. There is also a chance that the x-ray will disappear completely, creating in its stead two electrons, positive and negative. This would use up about 1 Mev to provide the mass, and the surplus x-ray energy would be divided between electron and positron as kinetic energy. The positron, in turn, will lose this kinetic energy by heating up material or exciting it to radiate. When it comes to rest, it will merge with an electron in the material, annihilating both of them. Their total rest mass of 1 Mev turns into the energy of two x-rays going in opposite directions, each with $\frac{1}{2}$ Mev.

Such an electron x-ray *shower* is shown in the bubble chamber photograph in Plate IV. As this complicated sequence proceeds, step by step and from beginning to end, the total mass-energy is conserved.

CONSERVATION OF MOMENTUM

Another simple combination of the basic variables remains constant throughout an interaction. For low velocities, the product of mass and velocity is defined as the *momentum*. There is a definite direction in space involved, and not only the magnitude but also this direction must be maintained.

In particle reactions this compound variable is often easier to measure and more meaningful than either the mass or velocity separately. For velocities close to that of light, the simple product is no longer accurate. The most general expression is

$$p = \frac{\sqrt{E^2 - (m_0 c^2)^2}}{c},$$

where p is the momentum and E is the total energy. For the case of a photon or neutrino with zero rest mass, the expression reduces to $p = E/c$. Thus particles can have momentum without having any rest mass at all. Photons can indeed exert force, which is merely the transfer of momentum. This is seen on the microscale in the Compton effect, the billiard-ball collision of a photon with an electron (Fig. 39).

In the figure, the momentum conservation in the x-direction requires

$$\frac{h\nu}{c} = \frac{h\nu'}{c} \cos \theta + \frac{m_0 v}{\sqrt{1 - v^2/c^2}} \cos \phi.$$

Momentum conservation in the y-direction requires

$$0 = \frac{h\nu'}{c} \sin \theta - \frac{m_0 v}{\sqrt{1 - v^2/c^2}} \sin \phi.$$

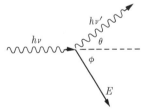

Energy conservation requires

$$h\nu = h\nu' + \frac{m_0 c^2}{\sqrt{1 - v^2/c^2}} - m_0 c^2.$$

FIG. 39. Compton effect.

There are three equations and four unknowns: θ, ϕ, ν, ν'. By changing the ν to c/λ, squaring the equations, and solving for θ, we get

$$\lambda' - \lambda = \frac{h}{m_0 c} (1 - \cos \theta).$$

The change in photon wavelength is a simple function of the deflection angle.
On the macroscale, the transfer of momentum from massless particles is observed in the spectacle of a comet's tail, which is always blown away from the sun by the streaming pressure of light and other particles.

The general expression for momentum reduces to the familiar one if the velocity is low compared with that of light, so that the kinetic energy equals $\frac{1}{2}m_0v^2$. In this case, the total energy is $E = \frac{1}{2}m_0v^2 + m_0c^2$ (see Section 3). The general expression for momentum then becomes

$$p = \frac{\sqrt{E^2 - (m_0c^2)^2}}{c} = \frac{\sqrt{(\frac{1}{2}m_0v^2)^2 + (m_0c^2)^2 + 2(\frac{1}{2}m_0v^2)(m_0c^2) - (m_0c^2)^2}}{c}$$

$$= \frac{\sqrt{(\frac{1}{2}m_0v^2)^2 + 2(\frac{1}{2}m_0v^2)(m_0c^2)}}{c}$$

$$\approx \frac{m_0vc}{c} = m_0v \quad \text{if} \quad \frac{1}{2}m_0v^2 \ll m_0c^2.$$

In analyzing a particle collision such as that in the Compton effect, the assumption is made that momentum is conserved. Originally all the momentum is in the horizontal direction to the right. After the collision there is evidently momentum of one particle in the upward direction while the other particle has momentum in the downward direction. Since there was no momentum up or down in the first place, there must still be none. Total momentum up must just equal total momentum down. The original momentum of the proton must still exist in the sum of the momenta to the right of all the resulting particles.

As an example of the importance of this conservation law, note that an x-ray of one Mev cannot in free space change into an electron pair, although all other rules would be satisfied. The x-ray carries momentum:

$$p = \frac{E}{c} = \frac{1\,\text{Mev}}{c} = \frac{1.6 \times 10^{-13}\,\text{j}}{3 \times 10^8\,\text{m/sec}} \approx 5 \times 10^{-22}\,\text{kg} \cdot \text{m/sec}.$$

This is an appreciable momentum on the particle scale. It is the same that an electron would have with a kinetic energy of about 0.8 Mev. Now if the x-ray turns all its energy into the mass of the electrons, there will be none left over to provide kinetic energy and so the electrons will have no momentum. Since the momentum cannot just disappear, the reaction does not take place. A more detailed calculation shows that even with higher x-ray energy the momentum balance cannot be made right for pair production in free space. The reaction takes place only in the neighborhood of a nucleus or electron which can share some of the spare momentum.

CONSERVATION OF ANGULAR MOMENTUM

The various dynamic properties of motion along a straight line have their counterparts in rotational motion. The most important of these is angular momentum, which can be so defined that it is considered a strictly conserved

(a)   (b)

Fig. 40. (a) Angular momentum = mvr. (b) Both wheel and disk have the same mass, radius, and rotational velocity, but the wheel has greater angular momentum than the disk.

quantity of an isolated system. Angular momentum has properties which differ materially from those of linear momentum. For an object which is being swung in a circle, for instance, the length of the radius has something to do with the rotational momentum. The combination of variables which defines the conserved quantity is simply mvr, where m is the mass, v the linear velocity, and r the perpendicular distance from object to the turning center (Fig. 40).

Another expression for this is sometimes more revealing. For circular motion the radius r and velocity v are related by the frequency f, the number of revolutions per second, thus,

$$f = \frac{v}{2\pi r}.$$

In terms of the frequency, the angular momentum is given by

$$mvr = 2\pi f m r^2.$$

The importance of the *shape* of the object is particularly apparent in this expression. Even if two objects with the same mass are rotating with the same frequency, their angular momentum may be quite different. For instance, if a bicycle wheel and a solid disk of the same radius and mass are rotating at the same rate, the wheel will have more angular momentum. Most of the mass is concentrated on the rim where r is the largest.

If an object is rotating freely and its shape changes, the frequency must also change if the angular momentum is to remain constant. This is the first thought of an alert observer watching a pretty skater twirl faster and faster on one blade. She starts spinning slowly by balancing on one blade point and pushing on the ice with the other skate (Fig. 41). This torque gives her angular momentum which will now remain constant, except for friction. Being an experienced skater, she starts with her arms outstretched, putting some of her total mass far away from her axis of rotation. After the spin begins she draws in her hands, concentrating the mass close to the axis. Since r of some parts decreases, her angular velocity has to increase. To slow down, she need merely stretch out her arms again.

Normally we think of angular momentum in relation to spinning objects. The earth has angular momentum about its spin axis and also the sun-earth

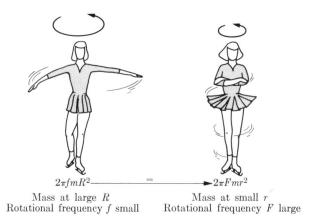

$$2\pi fmR^2 \xrightarrow{\hspace{1cm}} = \xrightarrow{\hspace{1cm}} 2\pi Fmr^2$$

Mass at large R Mass at small r
Rotational frequency f small   Rotational frequency F large

FIG. 41. Angular momentum conserved although angular frequency changes.

FIG. 42. Angular momentum of one object passing another.

system has angular momentum because of the annual revolution of the earth. But there is also angular momentum associated with one object which is only passing another. Two skaters who approach each other on a glancing collision course will set each other whirling if they touch (Fig. 42). Since they clearly have angular momentum *after* they meet, we must be able to assign an equal amount to their earlier motion if we are to maintain a conservation law.

A comet approaching the sun must maintain a constant product of mrv where r is the perpendicular distance of nearest approach, not the distance between comet and sun (Fig. 43). It cannot therefore fall into the sun, reducing r to zero, unless there are forces involved *not acting through the center of the sun* to produce a torque on it.

The *direction* of angular momentum remains constant also, unless it is changed by an appropriate torque. Otherwise we would all fall off our bikes. The spinning wheels violently resist any force which tends to make them fall over. In fact, instead of falling over, they react by turning left or right, as everyone knows who has ever ridden a bike no-hands. To turn to the right, you lean to the right.

The angular momentum of a solar system or of an atom is the total of all the separate spins and revolutions of its members. If some are clockwise and others counterclockwise, they will act to cancel each other. In the case of the solar

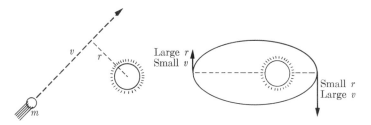

Fɪɢ. 43. Angular momentum of comet in orbit around sun. The (vector) product mrv ($r \times mv$) must remain constant.

system, the spins and revolutions are plain to see and, since we are so accustomed to them, easy to understand. Spinning electrons and atomic orbits require a more sophisticated view. We can never plot such motions in our everyday way. The electron must be considered to be a point in some theories; yet how can a point spin? The position of the electron within the atom can only roughly be localized, so that it is certainly incorrect to picture it as following a prescribed orbit. Nevertheless, as we have seen, the assignment of intrinsic spin and orbital angular momentum to the electron produces a theory which is successful in correlating all known experimental facts about the atom.

In particle interactions we must insist that the total angular momentum of a system remains constant. Each of the participating particles may have intrinsic spin even though they are at rest with respect to each other and have no relative angular momentum. For example, when a positron finally slows down in material it captures an electron. For a brief time, an "atom" is formed with the positron as nucleus. Of course, the nucleus in this case has the same mass as the electron and so really the two are distributed about their common center of mass. When they capture each other the only angular momentum involved is that due to their spins of $\frac{1}{2}\hbar$ each. These can be lined up together or opposed, leaving total angular momentum 1 or 0. The annihilated mass turns into the electromagnetic energy of photons each of which has intrinsic spin of $1\hbar$. One photon alone cannot be produced, because this would carry off linear momentum where originally there was none. So at least two photons must come off, and in opposite directions. Their individual spins might be in the same direction or opposed, yielding total spin of 2 or 0. Only the latter is possible since the electron-positron system has angular momentum of either 0 or 1. This is the most usual case, and experiments have demonstrated that the resulting gamma rays are polarized in the proper direction. But there is one other possibility. If the electron-positron spins are aligned, leading to total spin one, three photons can be emitted. Such a combination can conserve linear momentum and also combine the three spins of one each to allow a total of one. This three-photon annihilation is indeed observed but with a frequency down by a factor of one thousand compared with the usual two-photon production.

There is an important peculiarity of angular momentum which we pointed out in Section 3. In discussing energy or linear momentum we had no need for a basic natural unit of these quantities. A particle can have an energy of 1 ev or 0.465 ev or any other fraction or multiple. But the intrinsic spins of most particles are either 0, $\frac{1}{2}\hbar$, or $1\hbar$, and the relative angular momentum must always be 0, or 1, or 2, or some higher integer times $\hbar$. (Some of the short-lived resonance particles described in Section 8 have higher values of intrinsic spin but still integral or half integral.) In other words, angular momentum is quantized, even as electric charge is. The basic unit is Planck's constant h divided by 2π. (Planck's constant h is associated with frequency in terms of cycles or revolutions per second, while $\hbar = h/2\pi$ is associated with frequency in terms of *radians* per second. There are 2π radians in one full revolution.) Since the value of $\hbar$ is so extremely small ($\approx 10^{-34}$ kg·m^2/sec) we observe the quantum nature only in particle reactions. If a world could exist with $\hbar = 1$, rotating objects of human size would have strange behavior. A 1 kg stone whirled on a string one meter long could rotate only at frequencies in cycles per second of 0, $1/2\pi$, $2/2\pi$, $3/2\pi$, etc. Furthermore, the swing could occur only in certain discrete directions, spaced so that the change of angular momentum from one direction to the next would involve a change of $1\hbar$ $\left(1 \text{ kg} \times (\text{m/sec}) \times \text{m}\right)$ in this case. Bicycles could move only at integral multiples of some basic speed, determined by the size and weight of their wheels and could turn only through certain discrete angles.

The relative angular momentum of two particles makes itself apparent in conditions which allow or forbid certain types of reactions. The analysis of scattering experiments consists of explaining how many particles in a certain type of collision will be deflected through various angles. Such angular distributions are strongly dependent on the angular momenta of the particles involved. For example, protons colliding with protons interact through both electromagnetic and nuclear force fields. The target protons can have their spins oriented either with or against the approaching protons. However, two protons with spins aligned cannot exist in the same region because of the Pauli exclusion principle. A head-on collision, with no angular momentum due to their relative motion past each other, is therefore forbidden. It is allowed, however, if the two spins are opposed. With protons bombarding neutrons, this prohibition does not exist. The analysis of the amount of scattering and its angular distribution is consistent with this picture.

CONSERVATION OF ELECTRIC CHARGE

All experimental evidence indicates that electric charge is a particularly restricted type of quantized attribute. Particles have charge of $+1$, 0, or -1 times the basic charge e. (At least one of the resonance particles described in Section 8 can have a charge which is a larger multiple of e.) In terms of the standard engineering units, $e = 1.6 \times 10^{-19}$ coul. When electrostatic charge is produced by friction, the act is merely one of separating negative electrons from neutral molecules, leaving a positive charge of equal magnitude. When charged particles are created out of energy, an equal quantity of the opposite charge always appears.

Cosmologists have played theoretical games hypothesizing that the positive charge might be slightly larger than the negative. The electrostatic repulsion was tailored to explain the expansion of the universe. Recent experiments have shown that the magnitudes of the electron and proton charge cannot differ by more than one part in 10^{20}, which rules out this explanation of the expansion.

CONSERVATION OF BARYONS AND LEPTONS

The two groups of fermions, particles with half odd-integral spin, seem to maintain very special permanency. It is never possible to create out of energy a single baryon without also creating an antibaryon. Nor can either be annihilated separately. Such *dual* creation and destruction is seen in Plate V. The leptons are separately conserved. Although all the other conservation laws could be satisfied by a reaction producing single leptons and baryons, $(\gamma \nrightarrow p^+ + e^-)$ such a reaction is never seen. Lest such permanency should seem the only way to organize the universe, remember that there are no such conservation laws for the mesons or photons. At the present time, it appears that there are two separate kinds of leptons, muon and electron, each with its own neutrinos and each with its separate conservation law. Hopefully, a deeper understanding of the muon-electron problem will eliminate this redundancy.

Conservation laws of limited jurisdiction.   For an isolated system, energy-mass, momentum, angular momentum, electric charge, baryons, and leptons are conserved regardless of which of the four types of forces is involved. There are some other quantities which are conserved in some types of reactions but not in others.

CONSERVATION OF STRANGENESS

The very concept of strangeness was invented to explain why some reactions take place and others are not allowed. This, of course, is the nature of a conservation law. Using the strangeness numbers assigned to the particles in the chart, we find that the total strangeness of a system remains the same so long as only the strong nuclear or electromagnetic forces are involved. Thus in the high-energy collisions taking place in nuclear times of 10^{-23} sec, only the strong interactions are important. If a hyperon with negative strangeness is produced from a collision of particles with zero strangeness, then some particle with positive strangeness must also come out. If there is not enough surplus energy to create such a particle, a K-meson for example, then the hyperon will not be produced.

Once the hyperon is emitted it does not decay immediately into the strongly interacting pion and nucleon, although all the other conditions are suitable for such an event. The strangeness number would go from minus one to zero, and this is forbidden. Nevertheless, the decay does eventually take place through the agency of what we have called the *Weak Interaction*. Apparently the rule for such interactions is that the strangeness number can change by no more than one unit. The cascade hyperon (the xi, with strangeness of -2) can decay to a nucleon through the weak interaction but only in a two-step process, as shown by,

$$
\begin{array}{ccccc}
S=-2 & & S=-1 & & S=0 \\
\Xi^- & \rightarrow & \Lambda^0 & + & \pi^- \qquad \Delta S = +1 \\
& & \;\;\rightarrow \pi^- & + & p^+ \qquad \Delta S = +1 \\
& & S=0 & & S=0
\end{array}
$$

CONSERVATION OF PARITY

All of the conservation laws are associated with certain symmetries that appear in our *descriptions* of nature. It seems reasonable to demand that successful *descriptions* of a sequence of events or the shape of an object, usually in mathematical shorthand, should be independent: (1) of the position of the observer; (2) of the setting of his particular clock; (3) of the direction in which he is facing. For instance, imagine two observers facing each other (so that the right and left hand are reversed for them), ten feet away from each other, and with their clocks differing by one hour (Fig. 44). Each is to describe the sequence of operations when a constant force from a spring is applied to a block of mass m. Surely they can agree as to the magnitude of the force and the mass, since they are at rest with respect to each other. One, however, says, "The block starts from in front of me, at $x = 0$ at 9:00 o'clock and is accelerated toward observer two in the left direction which I will define as being negative."

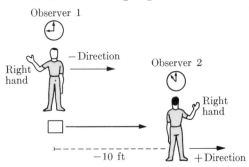

FIG. 44. Different observers with different coordinate systems will still agree on sequence of motion of block.

Observer two, on the other hand, claims, "The block starts at ten o'clock from a point minus ten feet from zero, traveling toward the right which I call positive."

Now, of course, there is no controversy here and the description of the predicted action is independent of the coordinates. Each will successfully predict the motion of the block. Even though their words may be different, they would agree about whether or not the block would suffer collisions or take part in other events. The examples can get far more complicated, but it is reasonable to assume that *physical events* should be quite independent of the position or orientation of an observer, and therefore the *descriptions* must be made similarly independent.

It is by no means obvious, but it can be proved, that if physical descriptions are independent of the origin of our coordinate system (which point we define as zero) then the quantity called momentum will be conserved. If the description does not depend on which direction we define as north or east (in other words if we can rotate our coordinate system arbitrarily) the angular momentum is conserved. If the particular setting of our clocks makes no difference to our physical laws, then energy-mass is conserved. If our laws are independent of the zero of electric potential, electric charge is conserved.

Fig. 45. (a) 180° rotation.
(b) Mirror reflection.

Another change of coordinates is possible and of interest. Suppose all the coordinates (x, y, z) were reversed to become $(-x, -y, -z)$. This is not at all the same as simply rotating the reference frame through 180°. The simple rotation would leave a right-handed man still right-handed although facing in the opposite direction (Fig. 45). But a reflection of the coordinates turns events into their mirror images. (The ordinary mirror transformation can be considered the product of the complete reflection plus a rotation of 180°.) Left-handed people become right-handed, clockwise becomes counterclockwise, and right-hand threads become left-hand threads.

Are there events in nature which depend on the right- or left-handedness of our descriptive system? If not, we should be able to find another conservation law. If so, we should be able to define once and for all what we mean by right hand or clockwise. Of course, on earth I can define right hand by raising my right hand. "When I face this direction, right is over here." But this is scarcely a universal definition. We might want to explain this for the benefit of a man on Mars.

Now note that if we can define right-hand, we have also defined clockwise, or vice versa. "To wind a coil clockwise, hold the cylindrical frame and start the wire around it at the end closest to you and at the top of the circle. The wire should now start out toward your right hand." Furthermore, such definitions are bound up with what we mean by north or south magnetic pole. If you look down a coil carrying electric current and the direction of the current appears clockwise to you, then the south magnetic pole is the end toward you (Fig. 46).

Can we now send these definitions to Mars? Since they can see a good deal about our planet there is no problem. They can observe which end of the planet we call north or "up," and then we need only tell them that from such a viewpoint we are traveling around the sun (and rotating on our axis) counter-clockwise. If they did not know which end is up, there would be a problem, of course.

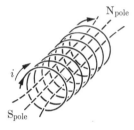

Fɪɢ. 46. Definition of N and S magnetic poles depends on the definition of clockwise and the sign of the electric charge.

Is there a truly universal definition of right-handedness? Can we send such information to people of a distant galaxy who cannot see our geometry at all but can only receive a sequence of signals? If any natural event has a prefer-ence for right or left (a corkscrew property) we can describe how to obtain this material or produce the phenomenon and our problem is solved. We could say, "Observe your roads. The cars are being driven on the right side." But they might be like the English. Or regardless of such perverseness, we could say, "Your hearts will in general be on the left side of your bodies." But in a distant galaxy? Maybe the people there have two hearts each. Or none. How about something unassociated with our peculiar human customs or construction? Some crystals have a natural corkscrew twist. There are, for instance, the two kinds of sugar-dextrose (right-hand) and levulose (left-hand). All we need do is send the recipe for producing the right kind of sugar. But it does not work that way. The chemical formula for the two is the same and when the crystals form, half twist to the right and half twist to the left.

Perhaps the particle interactions have a built-in direction sense. Consider a collision of two particles and the resultant scattering. Would we not expect different results in the forward direction from those in the backward direction or at right angles? There are indeed such differences and these angular dis-tributions provide our main clues as to the nature of the forces of interaction. For instance, in the classic experiment of Rutherford which determined the basic structure of the atom, most of the bombarding alpha particles went straight through the thin foil or were scattered by no more than a degree. A very few bounced at larger angles, including backwards. From such a distribution it was possible to deduce a picture of a solar-system atom with a small dense nucleus. This type of angular distribution is not the direction signal we seek, however. A line is indeed defined by the original direction of the bombarding particle, but around that line the scattering is completely symmetric. There are more scattered in the forward direction than in the back, but there are, at any particular angle, as many scattered up as down, as many to the right as to the left (Fig. 47).

Until 1956 it was a basic belief in physics that there was no natural event with a preferred screw sense. The many examples of such preference around us (roads, men, dextrose) could all be explained as local accidents depending on arbitrary previous conditions. A *mirror world* might seem peculiar to our prejudiced eyes but it would work just as well as our world, and all physical laws would be the same.

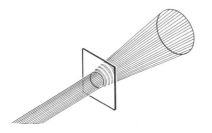

FIG. 47. Scattering is symmetric around axis, but, of course, is different forward from backward.

During the middle 1950's, a paradox had arisen in the interpretation of certain phenomena of strange particles. This was the θ-τ (theta-tau) paradox whose solution earned a Nobel prize for Lee and Yang. We will describe the problem later. Its resolution consisted of an analysis of various phenomena, just as we have been doing, to see whether or not some events did show a preference for clockwise rather than for counterclockwise. Of course, the ordinary evidence was as good as ever. Reactions involving the strong nuclear and electromagnetic forces (such as Rutherford's) had been sufficiently studied so that there was no question but that they were independent of handedness. But Lee and Yang soon realized that no experiments involving only the Weak Interaction had ever been done carefully enough under the right conditions to test this point. If the weak interactions were dependent on the screw sense of direction, it could explain the original θ-τ paradox and would furthermore imply the existence of other reactions showing the sense-dependent properties.

For instance, consider the arrangement of the first experiment that confirmed the ideas of Lee and Yang (Fig. 48). The radioactive Co^{60} nucleus has a large

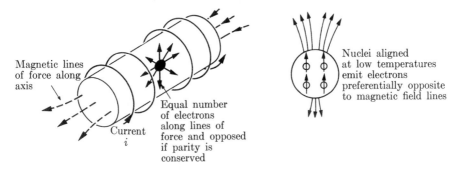

FIG. 48.   Nonconservation of parity in β-ray emission.

intrinsic angular momentum. Its spin is $\frac{7}{2}\hbar$ and provides a magnetic moment. Would it not be possible to align all the nuclei in a strong magnetic field and then examine the angular distribution of the β-rays? Under ordinary conditions, no effect at all would be expected because the thermal motion of the atoms would prevent any alignment. (There is no magnetic moment associated with the electronic aspect of this atom.) If the temperature is reduced to a few hundredths of a degree absolute, the thermal agitation is sufficiently reduced so that many of the nuclei have their spins pointing along the magnetic field lines. There is a distribution, of course, along the several possible directions allowed: $+\frac{7}{2}, +\frac{5}{2}, +\frac{3}{2}, +\frac{1}{2}, -\frac{1}{2}, -\frac{3}{2}, -\frac{5}{2}, -\frac{7}{2}$. Appreciably more line up in the positions along or partially along the field than against it. Under these circumstances, it is expected that more β-rays are emitted one way *and the other* along the field lines than at right angles. According to the traditional idea, however, there should be the same number emitted up as down, with the field or $180°$ opposed. If more electrons came out along the field than against it, it would be possible to send the following message to our extragalactic neighbor:

"Wind the coils of a magnet clockwise according to your definition (which may be opposite from ours). Now place Co^{60} in a cryostat in the magnetic field so that its temperature is close to absolute zero. The electrons from the β-decay will now come out preferentially in one direction along the field lines. (The magnetic field lines in the coil are axial.) Looking along the preferred direction of emission, the magnet coils will be wound in what we call the counterclockwise sense."

That would do it, *and indeed it does it.* A group of Columbia University and Bureau of Standards physicists working under Wu and Ambler found just this effect within half a year from the time Lee and Yang first proposed it. A screw sense can be defined; nature can distinguish between right and left hand.

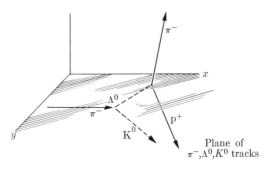

FIG. 49. Parity nonconservation in Λ^0-decay. Pi mesons from Λ^0-decay are preferentially on one side of the plane, thus defining "top."

Other experimenters soon showed that similar prescriptions for determining "handedness" could be made using the decays of some of the fundamental particles. In the decay of the Λ^0 hyperon into proton and π^-, the mesons are emitted preferentially on one side of a plane defined by the direction of the lines (Fig. 49). Once again, an orientation is defined, since, given a plane, we can now describe what we mean by "top" and "bottom."

The discovery of these phenomena and the implications concerning the lack of mirror symmetry in nature were almost as astonishing to physicists as if energy conservation could not be satisfied. But before we look too askance at this asymmetry of nature, let us remark that there is a catch. Antiparticles follow just the opposite handedness. If we send our prescription to Mars, we could be sure that they would have cobalt the same as ours and that their accelerators would produce Λ^0's the same way ours do. But if we attempt to establish a universal rule, we have no guarantee that our collaborator in a distant galaxy is not composed of antimatter, using anticobalt, and with his accelerator producing anti-Λ^0's. The reflection of space coordinates seems to be tied in with the reflection of charge, turning particle into antiparticle. There appears to be symmetry in the world only for the product of both effects together.

We have not yet defined any conserved property that is related to this symmetry of space reflection, or that is violated when symmetry does not exist. As is really true with all the other conservation laws, this conserved property is more a characteristic of our *description* of phenomena than of the phenomena itself. Such an appearance only emphasizes the nature of the game we are playing where our attempt is to manufacture rules and discover regularities that are consistent with as large a range of experience as possible. A group of numbers, signifying certain attributes, in a certain sense *is* the particle it describes, for it codifies all the complex interactions that we have associated with the particle.

In the classical description of events we might specify the position and velocity of a particle at a particular time. For instance: the position $x = x_0 + vt$. This tells us that the particle at time zero ($t = 0$) was at position x_0, and that it is traveling to the right (positive x) with a velocity v. Assuming we know that the time t is the time after zero on our stop watch, we can now locate the object at any future time.

The quantum mechanical description of a particle or event is more complicated, as we might expect, because of the problem of not being able to measure both the position and the momentum precisely. Where this indeterminancy is an important feature, all we can predict about events is the probability of finding a particle at some position at some time. Our mathematics, therefore, should give us a *probability function*. We get this by taking the solution to the mathematical equation describing the process, and, among other things, squaring this solution. The solution itself is called the "wave function." The process is familiar to us from dealing with wave equations of the electromagnetic field. A solution to these equations is obtained in terms of E, or B, the strength of the electric or the magnetic fields. The energy density, however, is proportional to $(E^2 + B^2)$.

Now if we insist that the *probability* be independent of whether we describe the position as $(+x, +y, +z)$, or $(-x, -y, -z)$, we have only two choices for the wave function itself. The mathematics of the function must be such that if all the (x, y, z)'s are changed to $(-x, -y, -z)$'s the function is either unchanged or simply equal to minus the original. In either case, the *square* of the function will remain the same.

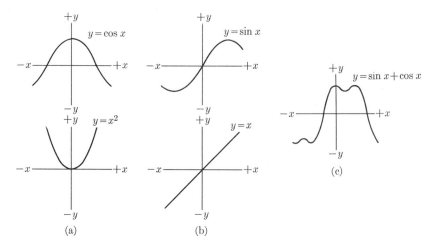

FIG. 50.   (a) Even symmetry, $f(x) = f(-x)$; (b) odd symmetry, $f(x) = -f(-x)$; (c) function without definite parity.

The graphs of several functions are shown in Fig. 50. The ones in (a) are defined as being *even* because $f(x) = +f(-x)$. The functions are symmetric about the y-axis. On the other hand, the ones in (b) are *odd* because they are antisymmetric. $f(x) = -f(-x)$. The *squares* of the functions, however, are independent of whether the values are taken at $+x$ or $-x$.

This characteristic of the mathematical description is called parity. Not all mathematical functions have definite parity, for example, $y = \sin x + \cos x$, as shown in (c). But for the overall description of simple particles, we can always choose functions which have either odd or even parity. Which we choose depends on the geometry of the interaction and in some cases on the particles themselves.

In describing complex molecules, such as the sugars, we must use a sum of wave functions, some with odd parity and some with even. The total is neither even nor odd. The complexity is just what is required in describing a system with a definite handedness. An event described by a function with parity either even or odd must be independent of the reflection of coordinates and so cannot exhibit any handedness.

Now the conservation law arising from space reflection symmetry is this: The *parity* of an isolated system cannot change; it will remain either even or odd. Any operation or sequence of events which will cause an asymmetry in the behavior of a system will also change the parity of the mathematical description. For example, consider a particle at rest which is decaying. Before the decay, the particle can be described by a wave function with a definite parity. The process which changes the particle to its decay products can be described by a mathematical expression which changes the original wave function to the final one. Any process that produces an asymmetry, such as north preferred over south, can be described only by mathematics that will change the parity of the final wave function. *Thus, by insisting that all physical processes conserve parity, we are insisting that there can be no processes which produce a preferred space orientation.* This conservation law was assumed to be as inviolate as that for charge or energy. Now we realize that only the strong and electromagnetic forces conserve parity. The Weak Interaction seems to violate it every chance it gets.

The realization that parity need not be conserved came as the solution to a problem that at first appeared to be an entirely different matter. During the early 1950's there was discovered the bothersome behavior of K-mesons, which we have already referred to as the θ-τ paradox. As in the case of other particles, special names had been given to certain decay modes before the particle itself was well known. One of the earliest appearances of K-mesons was observed as a triple meson decay (Plate VI). For several years this was called the τ-meson. Actually only 6% of charged K-mesons decay into three charged pions, but the triple tracks were so easy to see that at first a great deal of work was done analyzing them. Three times as many K's decay into just two π-mesons, one charged and one neutral (Plate VII). These were called θ-mesons. It is evident that such events are harder to find and recognize. In the case of the three visible tracks, their identity as π's and their energy can usually be measured very accurately. With this information, the mass of the parent τ is completely determined. With the two-pion decay, analysis is not much more complicated. The neutral partner must, according to the standard conservation laws, have a definite momentum. If the nature and energy of the one visible track can be measured, there is very little choice left for the values of the other parameters. As such measurements were made, it became more and more certain that the mass of the θ was the same as the mass of the τ. Furthermore, everything else about them seemed the same, including the mode of production and their lifetimes. It was not inconceivable, of course, that there could be just one particle but two decay modes. Indeed, the K-meson can decay into many other products including electrons and mesons.

The embarrassing feature of the θ-τ decay lay in the question of the parity of the parent K-meson. Experiments had shown that the π-meson must have odd *intrinsic* parity. We emphasize the word *intrinsic* because the overall parity of a function which describes a meson which is interacting with a proton, for example, might be odd or even, depending on the relative angular momentum of the two particles. The function which describes relative angular momentum of $0, 2, 4 \ldots \hbar$ has even parity, and that which describes states with $1, 3, 5 \ldots \hbar$ has odd parity. This arises in the same way that a sum of *sin* functions is odd, but a sum of *cos* functions is even. However, besides the symmetry arising from the geometry of the interaction, it is necessary to multiply the complete function by an odd term to describe the π-meson itself. Thus if the geometrical symmetry is odd, the total parity will be even; but if the geometry would produce even symmetry, the overall parity is odd.

Now then, what is the intrinsic parity of the K-meson as it decays into pions? Since in the θ mode only two pions come out, necessarily in opposite directions and so necessarily with zero relative angular momentum, the combination of the two odd-parity pions must be even. The triple pion decay is more complicated because there can be relative angular momentum in the geometrical distribution of the three particles. Analysis of the angular distribution of many such decays, combined with the fact that the intrinsic parity of three odd pions is odd, led to the certain conclusion that the τ had odd parity. The paradox was, then, that one and the same particle appeared sometimes to have even parity and sometimes odd. The resolution of this paradox seems obvious enough now, but it required a bold suggestion only a few years ago that perhaps in this weak interaction parity need not be conserved.

CONSERVATION OF ISOTOPIC SPIN

The isotopic spin of a particle seems to play a major role only in strong nuclear interactions. We presented the concept of isotopic spin as a convenient way of labeling particle multiplets: neutron, proton; and π^+, π^-, π^0. In the very word, multiplet, we imply that these systems are simply different aspects of the same particle. The members of a multiplet differ from each other in electric charge and to a slight extent in mass. These effects become apparent only when the electromagnetic interaction is observed. The original notion that the nuclear force was independent of the electric charge came from observations of energy levels in nuclei. The evidence is particularly striking in the "mirror" nuclei. These are found among the light elements and consist of pairs of nuclei having the same odd number of nucleons but with the proton-neutron number switched. Examples are: H^3-He^3, Li^7-Be^7, Be^9-B^9, B^{11}-C^{11}, C^{13}-N^{13}. In each case, the nuclei are identical except that x protons and y neutrons become y protons and x neutrons. The binding energies and excited states within each pair are almost the same, and the differences can be accounted for exactly by the known electromagnetic effects. The nuclear binding force is independent of whether the nucleon is a proton or neutron, so long as the reaction takes place with the same spin arrangement. As was pointed out earlier, the proton-proton and the proton-neutron scattering is the same as far as the pure nuclear interaction goes, although the electromagnetic effect and the spin orientation play major roles in the final results.

These phenomena can be described simply by stating that in the *strong nuclear* interactions, *total isotopic spin* is conserved. The law is a very special one since it can be violated by the electromagnetic and weak interactions. Let us analyze some examples:

$$(1) \qquad \text{p} \quad + \quad \text{p} \rightarrow \text{p} + \text{p} + \pi^0$$
$$I = \tfrac{1}{2} \qquad \tfrac{1}{2} \qquad \tfrac{1}{2} \qquad \tfrac{1}{2} \qquad 1$$
$$I_3 = +\tfrac{1}{2} \quad +\tfrac{1}{2} \quad +\tfrac{1}{2} \quad +\tfrac{1}{2} \quad 0$$

First of all we will see in all the strong and electromagnetic reactions that the third component of isotopic spin (I_3) is conserved. I_3 is related to the electric charge

$$Q = e\left(I_3 + \frac{b}{2} + \frac{S}{2}\right),$$

and the charge must be conserved. There is a change of I_3 only when there is a change in strangeness, and this can happen only in the weak interactions.

Secondly, remember that in combining isotopic spins, we use the same rules as for ordinary spin. It might appear at first that the two initial protons of this example could have total isotopic spin of *one* or *zero*. The *total* third component, however, is *one*. The vector cannot be less than one of its components and so the original total isotopic spin must be *one*. On the right-hand side we can arrange total isotopic spins of 2, 1, or 0. Again, the total I_3 is *one*, ruling out $I = 0$. The conservation law can be satisfied with the final $I = 1$.

(2) $$\pi^0 \quad \rightarrow \gamma + \gamma$$
$$I \;= 1 \qquad \text{no } I$$
$$I_3 = 0$$

In this decay of the neutral meson, I_3 is conserved since the process does not involve the weak interaction. Obviously, however, the total isotopic spin changes. The decay occurs (in a complicated way, as we shall see later) through the electromagnetic forces which do not conserve isotopic spin.

(3) $$\Lambda^0 \quad \rightarrow \pi^- + p^+$$
$$I \;= 0 \qquad 1 \qquad \tfrac{1}{2}$$
$$I_3 = 0 \qquad -1 \qquad +\tfrac{1}{2}$$

The decay of the Λ^0 is a weak interaction which can bypass several conservation laws. The π^- is emitted preferentially in one direction from the plane defined by the Λ^0 and the bombarding particle which produced it. Thus parity is not conserved. The value of I_3 of the Λ^0 is necessarily 0, but the total I_3 of the decay products is $-\tfrac{1}{2}$. *Charge*, however, is conserved which in this case means that *strangeness* cannot be. Finally, no combination of $I = 1$ and $I = \tfrac{1}{2}$ can produce a net isotopic spin of zero, which the Λ^0 has to begin with.

(4) The standard method of learning about the interaction of two particles is to shoot one at the other. The simplest feature to be measured is the number of times a collision occurs. If one-tenth of a beam of π-mesons fails to get through a target containing 10^{24} hydrogen atoms per square centimeter of bombarding surface, then the interaction area of each event must be 10^{-25} cm^2. This *total cross section* depends on the energy of the π-mesons. The interaction is primarily due to the strong nuclear forces; the electromagnetic effect of the charges can be taken into account separately.

The types of reaction possible are different for (π^-, p) than for (π^+, p) collisions. At energies low enough to avoid multiple π or strange-particle production, the π^+ collision is limited to

$$
\begin{array}{ccccc}
& \pi^+ & + \; \text{p} & \to \pi^+ & + \; \text{p} \\
I \; = & \tfrac{1}{2} & \tfrac{1}{2} & 1 & \tfrac{1}{2} \\
I_3 = & +1 & +\tfrac{1}{2} & +1 & +\tfrac{1}{2}
\end{array}
$$

The π^+ just bounces elastically from the proton, changing its direction and giving up some energy. The π^-, however, can do this or exchange charges with the proton in the process

$$\pi^- + \text{p} \to \pi^- + \text{p}$$

or

$$\pi^- + \text{p} \to \pi^0 + \text{n}$$

$$
\begin{array}{cccc}
I \; = & 1 & \tfrac{1}{2} & 1 & \tfrac{1}{2} \\
I_3 = & -1 & +\tfrac{1}{2} & 0 & -\tfrac{1}{2}
\end{array}
$$

In these strong reactions, both I_3 and I must be conserved. In the case of the π^+ reaction, only one isotopic spin state is possible. Since $I_3 = \tfrac{3}{2}$, then the total isotopic spin must equal $\tfrac{3}{2}$. For the π^- collisions, however, $I_3 = -\tfrac{1}{2}$. The total vector I could equal either $\tfrac{3}{2}$ or $\tfrac{1}{2}$ and still have a component I_3 equal to $-\tfrac{1}{2}$. Since the strong nuclear forces depend only on the *total* isotopic spin, quite different effects should be expected from the π^- and π^+ experiments. The π^- results should be a combination of the π^+ which can occur only for $I = \tfrac{3}{2}$, and the special contribution due to the total isotopic spin $I = \tfrac{1}{2}$.

This is indeed the case. The graph in Fig. 51 shows the dependence of the cross sections on the energy of the bombarding particle. The π^- curve shares in a resonance effect due to the $I = \tfrac{3}{2}$ effect but then has its own peculiarities due to $I = \tfrac{1}{2}$ which the π^+ does not have.

(5) We should demonstrate the effect of isotopic spin with a clear-cut case where a reaction does not occur simply because to do so would violate the conservation of isotopic spin. All of the reactions cited so far, except for the missing behavior of the π^+, p cross sections, *do* happen. In the ones where total I is not conserved, we notice that the reaction is electromagnetic or weak. Consider now

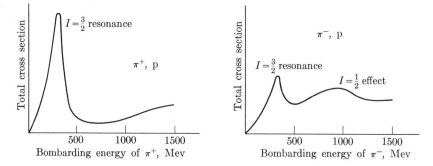

Fig. 51. Effect of isotopic spin on total collision probability.

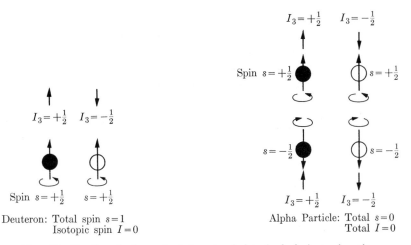

FIG. 52. Pauli exclusion principle extended to include isotopic spin.

the creation of helium by deuteron fusion in the following case:

$$H^2 \quad + \quad H^2 \rightarrow He^4 + \pi^0$$

$$I \; = \; 0 \qquad 0 \qquad 0 \qquad 1$$

$$I_3 = \; 0 \qquad 0 \qquad 0 \qquad 0$$

The isotopic spin of the deuteron or alpha particle is zero. The plausibility of this can be seen by considering the formula for the charge of a system: $Q = e(I_3 + b/2 + S/2)$. The deuteron has charge $+e$. The strangeness is zero and the number of baryons is two (proton and neutron). The real argument follows from the experimental observation that the proton and neutron are strongly bound only if their spins are aligned. If now they are close enough together to remain bound (an angular momentum of zero state), and we consider them simply as two fermions subject to the Pauli exclusion principle, then something about one must be different from the other (Fig. 52). This condition is satisfied by having the isotopic spin of one opposed to the other, leaving $I = 0$. In the case of He^4, there is only one way in which four nucleons can be grouped in the closest arrangement. Each nucleon has the attribute of spin $\frac{1}{2}$ and isotopic spin $\frac{1}{2}$. The arrangement shown in the diagram satisfies the exclusion principle and leaves the total isotopic spin (as well as ordinary spin) equal to zero. (Notice incidentally that the total ordinary spin of the deuteron is *one* and since that of the alpha particle is zero, they are both *bosons* and, as particles in their own right, not subject to the Pauli rule. This feature contributes to the queer behavior of liquid helium below 4° absolute.)

In the proposed fusion reaction, all other conservation laws can be satisfied. Only the conservation of isotopic spin would be violated, and this cannot happen in the strong nuclear interactions. The process has been sought under experimental conditions such that it could easily have been seen if it occurred. No evidence for the reaction was found.

Section 7. Roll Call of the Particles Stable against Rapid Decay through Strong Nuclear Forces

We have already described many of the properties of various particles, especially the electron. These descriptions, however, were given to illustrate the rules of particle behavior. In this chapter we will reverse that procedure. The characteristics of each particle will be given in terms of the parameters that have been derived. The roll will be called starting with the zero mass particles and proceeding toward those with higher mass.

THE MASSLESS BOSONS

1. The photon (γ). The photon is the agent of the electromagnetic field. We usually think of it as a particle only when the bundle of energy is localized in a region that is small compared with our detection apparatus. Thus, although radio waves could be characterized in terms of photons, the model is inconvenient in that frequency range. Visible light, or even infrared, can deliver energy concentrated enough to drive an electron out of metal. For such a process, the wave model of light is inconvenient, and the mental image of a localized photon seems more natural.

In any case, the energy of the photon is proportional to the frequency,

$$E = h\nu = hc/\lambda.$$

Here, E is the energy in joules; h is Planck's constant, 6.6×10^{-34} joules-sec; ν is the frequency in cycles/sec; c is the velocity of light, 3×10^8 meters/sec; and λ is the wavelength in meters. Sample calculations of wavelength, frequency, and energy for three different regions of the electromagnetic spectrum are shown on p. 47.

The photon carries momentum, p,

$$p = E/c = h\nu/c = h/\lambda.$$

In the final form, in terms of wavelength, the expression is identical with that for all the other particles. A common fallacy is to conclude that the photon must have mass since it has momentum. Of course, the *nonrelativistic* expression for momentum ($p = m_0 v$) cannot be used for electromagnetic radiation! The proper relativistic relationship between total energy and momentum, as was pointed out in Section 4, is

$$E = \sqrt{(m_0 c^2)^2 + c^2 p^2}.$$

Separating out the momentum, and expressing it in terms of the energy, we have

$$p = \frac{\sqrt{E^2 - (m_0 c^2)^2}}{c}.$$

This expression does away with the apparent paradox. It is not necessary for a particle to possess rest mass in order to exert momentum.

From another point of view, the photon cannot possibly have rest mass since, by definition, rest mass must be measured in some reference frame at rest with respect to the object. It is the fundamental hypothesis of the special theory of relativity that photons travel with the same speed, c, with respect to *any* frame of reference. Therefore, even in principle, a photon rest mass could not be measured, and the concept, therefore, is meaningless.

Whenever a photon is emitted, the angular momentum of the source, whether it be an atom or a nucleus, undergoes a change of one unit, $\hbar$. To conserve angular momentum, we must assign a spin of $1\hbar$ to the photon. All inverse effects where the photon is absorbed by a system are consistent with this assignment. Furthermore, even as the linear momentum of light can be demonstrated in the laboratory by its effect on a delicately suspended vane, the transfer of angular momentum from light to gross objects has been experimentally accomplished.

The photon is stable, since there is nothing into which it could transform without violating conservation laws. The integral spin (as opposed to half-integral spin $\frac{1}{2}\hbar$) implies that it is a boson. It is not subject to any exclusion principle forbidding the existence of more than one in the same region with the same properties, nor is there any conservation law forbidding the creation or annihilation of photons.

The photon can interact with particles only through their electric charge. Because of the way the world is arranged, most of these reactions involve electrons. It is not surprising, for example, that the energy of photons of visible light is a couple of electron volts. This is just the energy involved in chemical reactions, and so these photons are seen by our eyes and produce photosynthesis in plants. If a photon delivers all its energy to an atomic system and causes electron emission, the process is called "the photoelectric effect." Since the photon is absorbed, momentum must be taken up by the whole system. At higher energies, if the energy and momentum given to the atom is negligible compared with that given to the electron, the bombarded electron can be considered to be a free particle. In such a case, however, the photon cannot yield its full energy to the electron and so disappear. Conservation of momentum requires that the photon scatter with reduced energy, as shown in Fig. 39. This is called "the Compton effect," and clearly indicates the particle nature of the photon. The probability of such a collision decreases with energy.

When the photon has an energy of over 1.02 Mev, electron pair production can take place, as described in Section 3 and shown in Plate I. The probability of this reaction increases steadily with energy, eventually becoming more important than the Compton effect. Photons, or electrons, of very high energy can initiate cascades of such reactions. The primary photon will produce an electron pair, which share the original energy minus the 1 Mev for their creation. At high energy these will be projected forward within a cone of small angle. Eventually each will be swerved from its path by nuclei of the atoms through which it is passing. Since an accelerated charged particle radiates electromagnetic energy, the resulting photon continues in almost the same direction, if it has high energy, eventually producing yet another electron pair. Such a shower of electrons and photons is shown in schematic form in Fig. 53 and as it appeared in a bubble chamber in Plate IV. As the shower progresses, the number of particles, both photons and electrons, increases but the average energy decreases. Such showers are often produced in the atmosphere, starting with high-energy photons from the decay of π^0-mesons which in turn come from the primary cosmic ray bombardment at the top of the atmosphere.

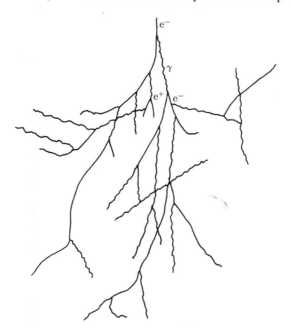

FIG. 53. Representative electron-γ cascade in a solid.

2. The graviton. The graviton is the agent of the gravitational force. When gravity is described by the same system used so successfully in electromagnetism (when the field is quantized), a quantum of gravitational energy is called for. It should have zero mass, propagate with the speed of light, and have spin of $2\hbar$. However, as was pointed out in Section 5, the gravitational interaction is extremely weak compared with the other three forces. Attempts are being made to detect "gravity waves," but so far there has been no success.

THE LEPTONS

1. Neutrino associated with electrons ($\nu_e, \bar{\nu}_e$). The original reason for postulating the existence of the neutrino was to save the conservation laws of energy, momentum, and angular momentum. The apparent failure of these laws had been observed in the β-decay of natural radioactivity. When one nucleus decays into another, a definite amount of energy is released, equal to the mass difference between the two nuclei. If an alpha particle is emitted (compound of two protons and two neutrons), it will have one of several definite energies. It may have the entire decay energy (minus the recoil kinetic energy of the nucleus) or one of several smaller values. However, if the alpha particle does not take the full transition energy, the daughter nucleus is left in an excited state and immediately emits a gamma ray. With all decays of this type, the total available energy is accounted for in terms of the energies of the decay products.

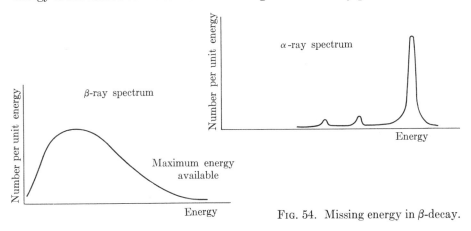

FIG. 54. Missing energy in β-decay.

In β-decay, however, when a positive or a negative electron is emitted or a negative electron is captured by the nucleus from the atomic system, the mass difference between the initial and the final states is not accounted for by any detectable products. The dissimilarity between the definite energies allowed in alpha decay and the spectrum of energies observed in β-decay is shown in Fig. 54. The maximum energy with which a few electrons are emitted is approximately the available energy due to the mass difference between initial and final states. Most of the electrons, however, carry off less energy than this. Where does it go? Elaborate calorimetry experiments were done during the 1920's to trap this energy, but without success. The energy conservation law appeared to have failed. Furthermore, analysis of the motion of the recoil nuclei showed that momentum was not conserved. Nor could angular momentum be accounted for! For example, the nuclear spin of $_6C^{14}$ is zero and the nuclear spin of $_7N^{14}$ is one. Yet this well-known decay apparently was

$$\underset{S=0}{C^{14}} \rightarrow \underset{S=1}{N^{14}} + \underset{S=1/2}{e^-} \,.$$

In 1933 Pauli suggested that all of these problems could be explained if each β-decay were accompanied by the emission of a neutral particle with small mass. Instead of β-decay being a two-body reaction, giving specific, discrete energies to the electron, the reaction would involve three bodies. This would explain the continuous spectrum of energy available to the electron and would account also for the missing momentum. The neutral particle must have spin of $\frac{1}{2}\hbar$ if angular momentum is to be conserved.

Fermi developed a theory of β-decay dependent on the existence of such a particle. Since it was clear that its mass would have to be smaller than that of the electron, Fermi called it the "neutrino." Experiments done during the 1930's and 40's demonstrated the consistency of the theory and further showed that the mass of the invisible particle must be close to zero. While there was no reason to doubt the existence of the neutrino, it was slightly embarrassing that the neutrino could not be detected once it was emitted. As the early calorimetry experiments had indicated, the neutrino is very penetrating, which means that it seldom interacts with anything. In going through the entire earth, a low-energy neutrino would stand only one chance in 10^{10} of causing a reaction.

In spite of the extremely small chance of a neutrino collision, this inverse effect was actually observed in 1956 by Reines and Cowan using the enormous flux of neutrinos from a nuclear reactor. Most of the neutrinos produced in a reactor come from β-decay following neutron capture. Although the reactor neutrons are mostly captured in nuclei other than hydrogen, the basic reaction is

$$n \rightarrow p + e^- + \bar{\nu}_e.$$

According to the principle of lepton conservation, *anti*neutrinos are produced. The inverse reaction is

$$\bar{\nu}_e + p \rightarrow n + e^+.$$

The annihilation characteristic of the positron is the key to the detection of such a rare event. As shown in Fig. 55, the detector consisted of enormous tanks of scintillator fluid viewed by photomultiplier tubes. The assembly was located in an underground room of one of the reactors at Savannah River. Although it was heavily shielded from the neutrons and the gamma rays of the reactor and

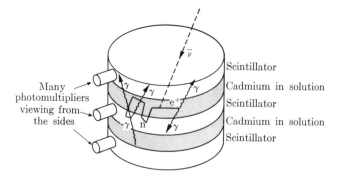

FIG. 55. Neutrino detection. Incoming antineutrino undergoes inverse β-decay in proton collision: $\bar{\nu} + p \rightarrow n + e^+$. The positron comes to rest and annihilates producing two photons which go in opposite directions. It is detected as a coincidence between two scintillator counters. The neutron wanders for several microseconds before being captured by a cadmium nucleus. The resulting isotope yields several γ-rays which are detected by the counters.

also from cosmic rays, many counts of neutrons would be recorded. The neutrino reaction which was being sought, however, produces a unique chain of events. The positron annihilation yields two gamma rays traveling in opposite directions. Two different segments of the tanks must respond in coincidence to these rays. Meanwhile, the neutron is wandering through the liquid, eventually slowing down and being captured. The unstable nucleus formed by the capture then decays through gamma-ray emission, giving signals delayed from the annihilation coincidence by several microseconds. With this special sequence of signals, the antineutrinos were clearly detected above the background of other events.

The fact that neutrinos are really different from antineutrinos was demonstrated by a negative result obtained in another experiment performed near a reactor. This time, since the goal was to produce electrons, *neutrinos* would be required to make the reaction go, as,

$$_{17}Cl^{37} + \nu \to {}_{18}A^{37} + e^-.$$

The reason for using this particular reaction is that A^{37} is unstable, decaying by capture of an electron from its atomic system. Furthermore, argon can be physically flushed from the original body of chlorine which is in the form of liquid carbon tetrachloride. Consequently, a very large amount (500 gallons) of CCl_4 could be exposed to the antineutrino flux from the reactor, and then the very small amount, if any, of radioactive argon produced could be concentrated in a small, sensitive detector. Conditions were made sufficiently sensitive so that the reaction could have been easily detected if neutrinos were the same as antineutrinos. It appears, however, that they are not.

The reason that neutrinos interact so seldom with other particles is that they are not subject to either the strong nuclear forces or to the electromagnetic force. They show up only in the Weak Interactions (although many Weak Interactions do not involve them). Since the Weak Interactions always violate parity, Lee and Yang proposed a revision of β-decay theory. In this theory, the neutrinos themselves are asymmetric with respect to reflection of the space coordinates. This, coupled with the fact that they travel with the velocity of light, means that their spin must be oriented either along the line of flight or opposite to it. If parity were conserved, there would be equal probability, but experiment has confirmed that the spin of the antineutrino is always in one direction, along the direction of motion, and the spin of the neutrino is always in the direction opposite to its motion. The antineutrino may be thought of as advancing like a right-handed thread, and the neutrino like a left-handed thread. In this theory, it is assumed that the neutrino mass is zero, and that, therefore, the neutrino must always travel with the velocity of light.

2. Neutrino associated with muons ($\nu_\mu, \bar{\nu}_\mu$). Neutrinos not only accompany electrons in β-decay, but also a neutral particle with mass less than $\frac{1}{7}$ electron mass (and presumably zero) is emitted with the muon in pi-meson decay,

$$\pi^- \to \mu^- + \bar{\nu}_\mu.$$

This event is shown in the bubble chamber picture of Plate VIII. The energy of the muon, as measured by the track length, is always the same. Such a specific division of energy in a decay can take place only if two bodies are involved. Since the muon cannot dash off by itself in one direction if momentum is to be conserved, there must be one neutral particle, leaving no trail, emitted in the direction opposite to the visible muon track. In the subsequent decay of the muon, the visible electron track indicates a different energy each time. In fact, the energy distribution of the electrons is a continuum much like that in classical β-decay. The reaction must be

$$\mu^- \to e^- + \bar{\nu}_e + \nu_\mu.$$

A small probability exists for a four-body decay which includes a gamma ray,

$$\mu^- \to e^- + \bar{\nu}_e + \nu_\mu + \gamma.$$

Note that already we anticipate a complicated situation by distinguishing between ν_μ and ν_e, neutrino associated with the muon and neutrino associated with the electron. At first it was assumed that these neutrinos were all the same. However, if they were, the muon should occasionally decay into an electron and a gamma ray, a two-body reaction,

$$\mu^- \to e^- + \underset{\text{virtual}}{(\bar{\nu} + \nu)} \to e^- + \gamma.$$

Note that in this situation there can be no direct interaction between the neutrino pair and the gamma ray. The neutrino is not affected by the electromagnetic field, and the gamma cannot respond to the Weak Interaction. Still the process might be expected if the neutrinos formed an electron pair through the Weak Interaction, and if then these were annihilated through the electromagnetic interaction to form the gamma. Such an event, however, has never been seen. Of course, if the two neutrinos are *not* antiparticles of each other, the two-body muon decay would not be expected.

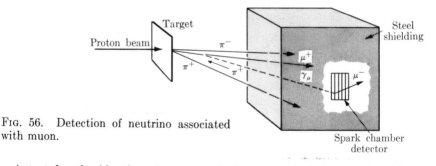

FIG. 56. Detection of neutrino associated with muon.

A test for the identity of muon and electron neutrinos would be to create inverse reactions with high-energy neutrinos and observe whether only muons or only electrons or both were produced. The reaction probability increases greatly with higher neutrino energy. As a practical matter, for high-energy neutrinos reactions associated with muons are easier to obtain than those associated with electrons. The experimental method is shown in Fig. 56. High-energy muons and their associated neutrinos are projected forward by pi-meson decays during flight. Only the neutrinos can get through the deep shielding. Of course, there will be neutrinos associated with electrons in the muon decay, but these will have lower energy and will be ejected at larger angles with a smaller chance of going through the spark chamber detector. Thus the reactions will be

$$\nu_\mu + n \to p + \mu^- \quad \overset{?}{\text{or}} \quad \nu_\mu + n \to p + e^-,$$

$$\bar{\nu}_\mu + p \to n + \mu^+ \quad \overset{?}{\text{or}} \quad \bar{\nu}_\mu + p \to n + e^+.$$

During an estimated exposure of 10^{14} neutrinos in a run taking 25 days of operation at Brookhaven Laboratory's Alternating Gradient Accelerator, about 50 pictures showing neutrino events were taken (Plate IX). Only a few of these showed tracks which might be interpreted as due to electrons, and these could be accounted for as the results of other reactions. It appears that the ν_μ cannot produce electron events and therefore is different from ν_e.

The mystery of the existence of two types of neutrinos is almost certainly the same as the mystery of the existence of the muon, which in every way except its mass (and associated neutrinos) is the same as the electron. Since the neutrinos are subject only to the Weak Interaction and presumably to the yet weaker gravitational force, experiments involving them are hard to perform. Because reaction probabilities increase with increasing energy, further experiments are being planned with the giant accelerators. In particular, since neutrinos are not involved in the nuclear or the electromagnetic forces, they may serve as a tool for the investigation of the Weak Interaction, as described in Section 5.

3. The electron (e^+, e^-). Since Section 3 was devoted exclusively to the electron, we will only summarize its properties here. It has a mass of 9.1×10^{-31} kg, which is equivalent to 0.51 Mev. Its charge is 1.6×10^{-19} coul, negative for the electron and positive for its antiparticle, the positron. The spin is $\frac{1}{2}\hbar$, making it a fermion and so subject to the Pauli exclusion principle. It is not subject to the strong nuclear force, but responds to the other three interactions. There is no way for it to decay and still conserve electric charge. Thus it is stable.

Because of its small mass, the electron attains relativistic speeds at comparatively low energy, above several hundred Kev (thousand electron volts). At high velocities, particles produce little ionization in the materials through which they pass. Therefore, the electron usually produces only sparse trails in emulsions, cloud chambers, and bubble chambers. Because of the small mass, it is easily influenced by magnetic fields. Electron tracks in chambers with magnetic fields are usually spirals. Near the end of its path, an electron usually undergoes numerous large-angle scatterings. These characteristics can be seen in the π-μ-e decay of Plate VIII and the electron-pair production of Plate I.

When a heavily ionizing particle, especially the doubly charged alpha, goes through a cloud chamber, the track often appears fuzzy with occasional curly tracks coming from it. These come from electrons which are knocked forward with energies of several Kev by the main ionizing particle. They were originally called *delta rays*. An example can be seen in Plate X.

The positron is as stable as the electron, but in our local universe a positron cannot last long. At low energy, when it comes close enough to an electron, the two will capture each other, forming a momentary atomic system. Annihilation follows with a half life of about 10^{-8} seconds if the electron and the positron spins are opposed. In this case, the total spin of the system is zero. Two photons are emitted in opposite directions in order to preserve momentum. Since their momentum must be equal, they share equally the mass-energy of the electrons, 0.51 Mev each. Since the original angular momentum was zero, the photons must be polarized so that their total spin is also zero. This is observed. In about one case in a thousand, the electrons annihilate with their spins aligned. The lifetime of such a system is 1000 times greater than for the case when the spins are opposed. With an original angular momentum of one unit, the system cannot produce only two photons, each with spin one. Instead, three photons are emitted, all necessarily in the same plane and with their polarizations such as to produce a total spin of one.

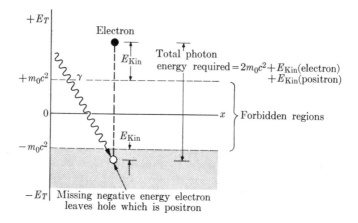

Fig. 57. Dirac negative energy states as pictorial explanation of positrons.

Historically, the positron is important because it was the first antiparticle predicted and observed. In 1928 Dirac worked out the relativistic quantum mechanical description of the electron. This work successfully called for a particle with spin equal to $\frac{1}{2}\hbar$, but also provided for the existence of such a particle in a negative-energy state. One interpretation of this is that all the negative-energy states are filled with electrons. Consequently, since there can be no transitions between the ordinary positive-energy states and those that are completely saturated, they do not affect our everyday world. However, if sufficient energy is supplied to lift an electron out of this negative-energy hole, the electron itself will have positive energy, and the hole that is left will have all the appearance of a positive electron. This pictorial model is shown in Fig. 57.

In 1932, Anderson obtained a cloud chamber picture of a cosmic ray particle whose track was curved by a magnetic field. If the direction of the track were known, the curvature would tell whether the particle's electric charge were positive or negative. Although most cosmic ray particles near the earth are in general heading from top to bottom, scattering can occur and the direction must be determined independently. The famous picture obtained by Anderson is shown in Plate XI. The particle must have had more energy before passing through the thin plate than it did afterward. Since its curvature is greater at the bottom of the plate, it must have been coming from the top. The known direction of the magnetic field indicated that the particle must be positive; the appearance of the track and the measurable amount of energy lost in the plate indicated that the mass of the particle must be close to that of an electron.

4. The muon (μ^+, μ^-). The muons as well as their associated neutrinos seem to have no useful function in the table of particles. In every way muons appear to be heavy electrons. Their interaction with the electromagnetic force is the same as that of the electrons, including such details as the relationship between spin and magnetic moment.

Muons form the so-called *hard* component of the cosmic radiation at sea level. The *soft* component, consisting of the tail end of electron-photon showers, is more easily absorbed and stopped. Since the muons take part in no nuclear interactions, they lose energy only because of electromagnetic ionization of the material through which they pass. Because their mass is 207 times as great as that of electrons, they are not so easily deflected by nuclei in their path and therefore radiate very few photons. At sea level, the flux of muons from the cosmic radiation is almost $1/cm^2/min$.

Muons are usually formed as the decay products of π- and K-mesons. There is low probability that muon pairs will be produced by gamma rays since it is hard to satisfy momentum conservation and still provide the necessary large rest mass. Electron pairs must be created in the vicinity of an atom or electron which can take up the surplus momentum lost by the photon in the change of its energy to electron rest mass. Muon pair production would require a very large transfer of momentum to a spectator system.

Although π- and K-mesons are the immediate products of the high-energy collisions of primary cosmic ray protons at the top of the atmosphere, their short half lives prevent them from traveling far. The muon has a lifetime of 1.5×10^{-6} sec, 100 times as long as that of the π. Even traveling at the speed of light, half of them should decay in a distance of 450 meters, which is no more than 1/50 of the distance from their origin to the earth. The relativistic dilation of time explains the anomaly. We observe that their decay times are longer than if they were at rest; in their frame of reference, the distance between origin and earth has shrunk by the same factor.

The spin of the muon is $\frac{1}{2}\hbar$, the same as that of the electron. When it comes to rest, the negative muon forms an atomic system, taking up positions near a nucleus appropriate to a very heavy electron. The energy levels are deeper than for an ordinary electron because the quantized radial positions are smaller. These systems have been analyzed by means of the x-rays emitted as the muon drops from one energy level to the next. In all but the light nuclei, the negative muons will be captured and absorbed into the nucleus in times shorter than the microsecond needed for decay. In carbon and lighter nuclei, decay will usually take place before absorption. The positive muons cannot be captured into an atomic system and so are always seen to decay.

The π-μ-e decay in Plate VIII shows the whole sequence of muon production and decay. Both pi-meson and muon came to rest before they decayed. This is evident from the nature of the track for the meson. As it slows down, the meson ionizes more and more heavily, leaving a thicker trail. At the very end of its range when the momentum is low, its trail is often wobbly. The short muon trail appears uniformly thick. Apparently the muon did not receive much energy from the π decay. The actual value can be found from a measurement of the range and the known characteristics of the bubble chamber. All the muons, from π decays at rest, have the same energy, indicating that a two-body process is involved. Assuming that the neutral body has zero rest mass, the division of energy between the two is easily calculated.

Available energy: $m_\pi - m_\mu = 140$ Mev $- 106$ Mev $= 34$ Mev

Momentum conservation: $p_\mu = p_\nu$

Energy of nonrelativistic muon: $E_\mu = p_\mu^2/2m_\mu$ $p_\mu = \sqrt{2m_\mu E_\mu}$

Energy of zero mass neutral: $E_\nu = cp_\nu$ $p_\nu = E_\nu/c$

Since $p_\mu = p_\nu$, $E_\mu = E_\nu^2/2m_\mu c^2$

Distribution of available energy: $E_\mu + E_\nu = E_\nu^2/2m_\mu c^2 + E_\nu = 34$ Mev

Since $m_\mu c^2 = 106$ Mev, $E_\nu = 29.5$ Mev

The muon's kinetic energy is thus 4.5 Mev.

THE MESONS

1. The pi-meson (π^+, π^-, π^0). The pi-meson is a first approximation to the nuclear interaction agent predicted by Yukawa in 1935. Like the exchange of photons which constitutes the electromagnetic field between two charged particles, the short-range nuclear force is created by the interchange of mesons. (See Fig. 35 and the accompanying description of nuclear force.) Because such interaction agents must be capable of being produced one at a time, there can be no conservation law about their number. They have spin zero, are not subject to the Pauli exclusion principle, and thus are bosons.

The particles found in the cosmic rays in 1937 by Anderson and Neddermeyer and by Street and Stevenson had about the same mass as that predicted by Yukawa. However, the very fact that they existed at sea level, having come through the whole atmosphere, indicated that their interaction with matter was slight. By 1947 it was clear that the cosmic-ray particle could not be the nuclear glue. At about the same time that theorists were proposing that the true meson might decay into the observed particle, the actual event was found in photographic emulsions which had been flown at the top of the atmosphere. Lattes, Muirhead, Occhialini, and Powell analyzed a track showing a π-μ decay. During the following year it became possible to produce pi-mesons at the Berkeley synchro-cyclotron.

The π^+ and π^- can be considered to be particle and antiparticle, although such a distinction is not so important as it is for fermions where a conservation law of particles must be satisfied. The π^0, then, is its own antiparticle. They are subject to all four interactions. The production process usually involves the strong nuclear force. If enough surplus energy is given to a nucleon system to provide the necessary mass, a meson can be materialized. The energy can, however, be provided through the electromagnetic force in the form of a high-energy photon. Pi-mesons are also produced during the weak decays of the hyperons or of the K-mesons.

The decay of the charged pi's must take place through the Weak Interaction, since the nuclear forces do not affect particles that are lighter than the pi, and no electromagnetic route is possible. For instance,

$$\pi^- \rightarrow e^- + \gamma$$
$$\underset{S=0}{} \quad \underset{S=1/2}{} \quad \underset{S=1}{}$$

would involve the creation of a single lepton and, furthermore, would not conserve spin. The actual decay route, with a half life of 1.8×10^{-8} sec, is

$$\pi^- \rightarrow \mu^- + \bar{\nu}_\mu, \qquad \pi^+ \rightarrow \mu^+ + \nu_\mu.$$

In about one time in 10,000, the alternative mode with an electron is seen,

$$\pi^- \rightarrow e^- + \bar{\nu}_e, \qquad \pi^+ \rightarrow e^+ + \nu_e.$$

The Weak Interaction is always observed between pairs of fermions. In this case, the primary particle is a boson. The process can go, however, by way of a virtual state. For times short enough to satisfy the Uncertainty Principle, the energy of the π can fluctuate enough to produce the momentary existence of a pair of nucleons. These may then produce, through the Weak Interaction, the products actually seen, for example,

$$\pi^+ \xrightarrow[\text{strong}]{} (p^+ + \bar{n}) \xrightarrow[\text{weak}]{} \mu^+ + \nu_\mu.$$
$$\underset{\text{virtual}}{}$$

The π^0 leads a much more transient existence. An electromagnetic decay route is open to it, because there is no electric charge to be conserved,

$$\pi^0 \rightarrow \gamma + \gamma.$$

The half life for this process is 0.7×10^{-16} sec. Its measurement is described in Section 8. It might seem that the π^0, having no electric charge or magnetic moment, should not be subject to the electromagnetic field. Once again, a virtual process must be responsible. The π^0 *is* strongly coupled with the nuclear field and, therefore, for brief times can exist as a nucleon pair. The pair then annihilates, producing particles which conserve momentum and energy. The most likely result is

$$\pi^0 \xrightarrow[\text{strong}]{} (\text{n} + \bar{\text{n}}) \xrightarrow[\text{virtual}]{\text{E-M}} \gamma + \gamma.$$

An alternative process, which occurs about once in 80 times, is

$$\pi^0 \to \gamma + e^+ + e^-.$$

The electrons, in this case, are called a Dalitz pair, named for the man who first calculated the process. In every 29,000 decays, two pairs of electrons will be produced without any photons.

The slight mass difference between the charged pi's and the neutral, can presumably be explained in terms of the electromagnetic self energy. The best determination of the difference is made by an analysis of the charge exchange reaction,

$$\pi^- + \text{p} \to \text{n} + \pi^0, \quad \Delta E = (m_{\pi^-} - m_{\pi^0}) - (m_\text{n} - m_\text{p}) \approx 4 \text{ Mev.}$$
$$\text{(at rest)}$$

The extra energy due to the mass difference, minus the energy difference between neutron and proton, gives kinetic energy to the neutron and the π^0. The much lighter π^0 takes most of this energy, which shows up as a spread of energy of the resulting decay photons. The resulting spectrum is described in Section 8.

2. The K-meson ($K^+, K^-, K^0, \overline{K^0}$). The K-meson is produced by the strong nuclear forces when particles interact at very short range. There is a great variety of decay modes. Many of these were first seen, although not necessarily understood, in cosmic ray experiments done during the late 1940's. As can be seen on the chart of the particles, the K^0 decays often produce two charged particles. These, along with decays of the Λ^0, were called "V particles," since that was their appearance in the cloud chamber pictures. An example of such a track can be seen in Plate XII. The fact that these strange particles must be produced in associated pairs was demonstrated at the Brookhaven Laboratory Cosmotron in 1953. From that time on, most of the investigation of particle physics was done at the big accelerators, and cosmic ray physics became more concerned with questions of space and cosmology.

A major task of the machine experiments was to unravel the various K-decay modes. Until about 1957 it was not clear that they were all due to the same particle. In particular, the three-pion decay shown in Plate VI was attributed to the τ-particle, and the two-pion decay was supposed to come from a different particle called θ,

$$\tau^+ \to \pi^+ + \pi^- + \pi^+, \qquad \theta^+ \to \pi^+ + \pi^0.$$

As the experimental results grew more precise, it appeared that θ and τ were alike in every way except their decay mode. This presented itself as the θ-τ paradox described in Section 6. The two different decay modes had different parity; the resolution of the paradox was that parity need not be conserved in the Weak Interaction.

The associated production of K-mesons with hyperons was explained in terms of a new conservation law, strangeness. In the Cosmotron experiments, K^+-mesons were produced but not K^-. Their mass is the same but their strangeness number is different. All the hyperons have negative strangeness. Since there was not enough energy available to produce antihyperons, the associated production required K-mesons with positive strangeness.

The K-mesons have spin zero, as can be seen from their decay products. They can decay into pi-mesons with spin zero, or into lepton pairs with spins which cancel.

The decay times of 10^{-10} to 10^{-8} seconds are convenient to measure. Particles traveling close to the speed of light for such times will have tracks from 3 cm to 3 meters long. Time dilation may increase these times and track lengths, but this range is easy to measure with cloud and bubble chambers or with counter telescopes.

Notice that the mass of 494 Mev is far more than three times the pi-meson mass of 140 Mev. If it were not for the necessity of conserving strangeness, the strong nuclear interactions would cause a decay into pi-mesons in 10^{-23} seconds. Electromagnetic decay routes are also available, but these too must conserve strangeness. Only the Weak Interaction can cause the decays.

The fact that K^0 is not the same as $\overline{K^0}$ produces behavior unlike that of any of the other particles. First of all, it makes the K a charge-doublet state with isotopic-spin of $\frac{1}{2}$. Secondly, a K^0 is available with both positive and negative strangeness. If sufficient energy is available during production processes, K^0 or its antiparticle can be produced to create the proper balance of strangeness. During the Weak Interaction decay, however, strangeness is not conserved,

$$K^0 \to \pi^+ + \pi^- \qquad \text{or} \qquad K^0 \to \pi^0 + \pi^0.$$

The decay mechanism for the K-antiparticle decay into the pi antiparticles should be identical with equal probability,

$$\overline{K^0} \to \pi^- + \pi^+ \qquad \text{or} \qquad \overline{K^0} \to \pi^0 + \pi^0.$$

The products are evidently identical! But since all these reactions can go in either direction if energy is available, it appears that during decay the particle and antiparticle would be the same thing even though during creation they are separated by their strangeness assignment.

The prediction was made by Pais and Gell-Mann that in these strange circumstances the decaying K^0 or $\overline{K^0}$ could be described as existing in a state with equal probability of being K^0 with strangeness $+1$ and $\overline{K^0}$ with strangeness -1. The quantum mechanical description of such a combined state consists of two terms which may be linked as a sum or a difference. When the decay probabilities are linked as a difference term, they cancel, yielding zero probability for decay into the two pi's. For the sum term, the probability is enhanced so that the decay takes place. This is an interference effect. A crude model of what happens is that either the K^0 or $\overline{K^0}$, having been produced, oscillates, through virtual processes involving the common π^+, π^- decay, between being K^0 and $\overline{K^0}$. There is then equal probability of its final decay into π^+, π^- or π^-, π^+. If the probabilities are in phase, both modes decay so that the π^+ from each reinforce, and the π^- from each reinforce. The decay takes place with the emission of real π^+ and π^-. On the other hand, if the probabilities are out of phase, the π^+ from one mode cancels the π^- from the other mode, and no real pi's are emitted.

The decay states are therefore a combination of the creation states, and vice versa. The decay states are given different symbols, K_1^0 for the constructive interference state yielding π^+, π^- decay, and K_2^0 for the state where the probability of π^+, π^- decay cancels. The decay time for K_1^0 is relatively fast, 0.7×10^{-10} sec. Since this easy decay is forbidden to the K_2^0, it has to wait for more complicated routes to occur. These three-body decays involve pi-mesons or combinations of pi's and leptons. The half life is about 4×10^{-8} sec.

The result of this strange resonance behavior is that once either K^0 or $\overline{K^0}$ is created, there is a 50% probability that it will decay with a half life of 0.7×10^{-10} sec. A beam of these will rapidly turn into a beam of K_2^0, as the K_1^0 die out with the two-pi decay. Further downstream, later in time, an almost pure K_2^0 beam will produce three-body decays. Yet another strange effect can occur. Neither K_1^0 or K_2^0 have definite strangeness, but both are combination states that can be described as half K^0 and half $\overline{K^0}$. The K_2^0 beam can therefore produce effects in nuclear collisions which require either positive or negative strangeness. The remarkable feature of this behavior has been experimentally confirmed. If K^0's are produced in association with Λ^0, they have positive strangeness. In subsequent nuclear collisions they therefore cannot produce Λ^0, which would require negative strangeness. However, if a beam of K^0's is allowed to travel some distance, the decay mode K_1^0 dies out, leaving mostly K_2^0. Each of these is composed equally of K^0 and $\overline{K^0}$. Now Λ^0 can be created, because $\overline{K^0}$ has negative strangeness.

3. The eta zero (η^0). The eta zero decays through the electromagnetic interaction into π^+, π^-, and π^0. The decay time is less than 10^{-16} seconds, which is not time enough for the η^0 to move a detectable distance from its point of origin before decay. In this respect it acts like the π^0. Since the final product of the η^0 is a trio of pions, all coming from the original collision point, its detection depends on the analysis of multipion events. The methods for doing this are described in Section 8. Most of the new particles discovered in this type of analysis are the so-called resonance particles, unstable even against strong nuclear decay.

There would seem to be no reason, from anything that we have said so far, why the η^0 should not be strongly coupled to its pion decay products. We would therefore expect that it should decay in nuclear interaction times of 10^{-23} seconds. The only conservation law which would allow an electromagnetic decay while forbidding a strong nuclear decay is that of isotopic spin. Since the η^0 is a singlet, it must have isotopic spin of 0. The pions have isotopic spin of 1, with π^+ having $I_3 = 1$; π^0 having $I_3 = 0$; and π^- having $I_3 = -1$. The trio could arrange themselves to have a total isotopic spin of 0, but the experimental evidence is that they do not.

THE BARYONS

1. The nucleons (p^+, n, $\bar{n}$, $\bar{p}^-$). The nucleons are the main constituents of nuclear matter, and thus of the mass of the world. According to our organizational scheme, the neutron and proton are basically the same particle, but in different isotopic spin states. They form an isotopic doublet of spin $\frac{1}{2}$, with the proton having $I_3 = +\frac{1}{2}$ and the neutron $I_3 = -\frac{1}{2}$. The electromagnetic field differentiates between them and presumably is responsible for the slight mass difference. To the nuclear force, however, they are the same particle.

The nucleon is a fermion, with spin $\frac{1}{2}\hbar$. It was realized long ago, however, that the magnetic moments of proton and neutron were different from those expected if the nucleons were simple point charges. In contrast, the magnetic moment of the electron agreed with the Dirac theory, except for an extremely small correction discovered and explained during the 1940's. Clearly, the very fact that the neutron acts as a magnet implies that it cannot be a *simple* spinning neutral particle. A magnet can be formed from a spinning charged particle but not from one without any charge at all. There must be internal currents. The explanation lies in the structure of the nucleons. Electron scattering from nucleons must be explained in terms of some regions which are positive and, in the case of the neutron, some regions which are negative. Perhaps the region at small radius might be considered to be the source of K-mesons, and the outer regions the source of pi-mesons. However, no such model yet proposed yields quantitative agreement with experiments. As will be discussed in Section 8, extremely short-lived mesons have been observed. Very likely the details of the nuclear force and nucleon structure must take into account these transient particles.

The proton is stable. Since no other conservation law forbids its decay into lighter particles, we explain the stability by inventing a law of Conservation of Baryons. Each baryon is assigned a baryon number of +1, and each antibaryon a number of −1. The total baryon number must be conserved. Thus a baryon-antibaryon pair must be created together, and the antibaryon annihilation must take a baryon with it.

Since the neutron is slightly heavier than the proton, it will decay into proton and electron with a surplus energy of 1.3 Mev. The half life is about 700 seconds. Within the nucleus, of course, the energy balance is entirely different. The strong nuclear forces continually exchange the role of protons and neutrons by the exchange of pi-mesons. To observe the free decay it is necessary to produce a sizable beam of neutrons, traveling slowly enough so that a few will decay over a convenient path length. Plenty of neutrons exist within and near a reactor, but the reaction, $n \rightarrow p + e^- + \bar{\nu}_e$, would be lost in the radiation background. A beam of slow (several thousand miles/hour) neutrons can be made to travel some distance into a low background region, and there the occasional decays are detected as a coincidence between electron and proton.

The early models of nuclear matter, after the experimental findings of Rutherford had been elaborated into the Bohr atom, were based on mixtures of protons and electrons. As the wave-particle theories were developed during the late 1920's, it became clear that electrons had no business being in an atomic nucleus. As was pointed out in Section 4, the Uncertainty Principle prevents a particle as light as the electron from being confined with reasonable energy to a region as small as the nucleus. Furthermore, the intrinsic spin of an atomic nucleus must be made up of the sum of the spins of the constituents. An even number of spin $\frac{1}{2}$ particles can produce only integral spin; an odd number must produce half-integral spin. If the nucleus of $_7N^{14}$ were composed of 14 protons (to account for the mass) and 7 electrons (to yield a net charge of $+7$), its spin should be half-integral. However, its measured spin is $1\hbar$. This is reasonable in terms of a nucleus consisting of 14 *fermions*, 7 protons and 7 neutrons.

When a neutron effect was first observed in 1930 by Bothe and Becker, they assumed that they were dealing with a very energetic gamma ray. When alpha particles from polonium bombarded beryllium, a penetrating radiation was produced. Joliot and Curie discovered that the radiation would knock protons out of paraffin with an energy of over 5 Mev. To do this, a gamma ray would have to have an energy of over 50 Mev. The alternative was pointed out by Chadwick in 1932. If the penetrating radiation consisted of electrically neutral particles with a mass about the same as that of the proton, the kinetic energy of the neutral particle would be a reasonable 5 Mev. It rapidly became clear that the existence of such a particle was consistent with many other experiments and cleared up the problems created by assuming that electrons were in the nucleus.

An example of neutron collisions in a helium filled cloud chamber is shown in Plate X. These neutrons had an energy of about 200 Mev, resulting from nuclear collisions of protons of slightly greater energy. Without the handle of an electric charge, high energy neutrons can be produced only by such indirect methods. Similarly, they can be detected only by the secondary detection of their collision products. In the picture shown, over 10,000 neutrons passed through the chamber during the sensitive time, but except for the two collisions they left the chamber undisturbed.

Although the nucleons are fermions and Dirac's analysis would call for the existence of their antiparticles, it was not clear that such complex structures would behave like electrons in this respect. In 1955 antiprotons were first detected by Chamberlain, Segre, Wiegand and Ypsilantis at the Bevatron in Berkeley. The reaction was

$$p \quad + \quad p \quad \rightarrow \quad p \quad + \quad p \quad + \quad p \quad + \quad \bar{p}$$
$$b = 1 \quad b = 1 \quad\quad b = 1 \quad\ b = 1 \quad\ b = 1 \quad\ b = -1$$

The original baryon number of 2 is conserved. The fact that the particle detected was actually an antiproton was determined in two ways. First of all, the products of the proton-proton collision had to pass through collimators and magnetic fields admitting only a narrow band of momenta for *negative* particles. Most of the particles coming through the system were π^--mesons. However, the few antiprotons of this particular momentum had a smaller velocity than the mesons, and so took longer to go through the complicated series of counters. The measured time of flight was appropriate for particles which had the mass of nucleons. An even more positive identification was made by exposing photographic emulsions to this composite beam. When an antiproton stopped, it annihilated, producing a "star" of meson tracks. This process, as photographed in a hydrogen bubble chamber, is shown in Plate III.

Since the creation energy for a nucleon pair is 1876 Mev, it might at first seem that it would have been possible to create such an event at the 3 Bev Cosmotron. The bombarding energy, however, must be much higher than the creation energy in order to conserve the bombarding momentum. We find here an example of the problem posed by the requirement that momentum be conserved. If the bombarding proton had only the 1876 Mev which is needed for creation of a nucleon pair, the energy could not all be used for the pair creation since then none of the resulting particles would have any energy or momentum. The momentum cannot be absorbed by the heavy target nucleus. At these energies, the bonds within the target nuclei are relatively unimportant. The collisions are, to a first approximation, between individual nucleons.

The most efficient way to distribute the bombarding momentum is for each of the four resulting protons to share it equally. Thus,

$$p_{\text{individual}} = \tfrac{1}{4} p_{\text{original}},$$

where p is momentum. Each of the final protons has the same energy in this case, E_i. The original kinetic energy of the bombarding proton must have been

$$E_0 = 4E_i + 2m_0 c^2.$$

The relationship between kinetic energy, total energy, and momentum is

$$E_{\text{kinetic}} = \sqrt{(m_0 c^2)^2 + c^2 p^2} - m_0 c^2.$$

Therefore,

$$cp = \sqrt{(E_k + m_0c^2)^2 - (m_0c^2)^2}.$$

Substituting this expression for momentum into the relationship above, and solving for E_i, we have

$$c^2p_i^2 = \tfrac{1}{16}(c^2p_0^2),$$
$$(E_i + m_0c^2)^2 - (m_0c^2)^2 = \tfrac{1}{16}[(E_0 + m_0c^2)^2 - (m_0c^2)^2],$$
$$= \tfrac{1}{16}[(4E_i + 3m_0c^2)^2 - (m_0c^2)^2],$$
$$2E_im_0c^2 = \tfrac{1}{2}(m_0c^2)^2 + \tfrac{3}{2}E_im_0c^2,$$
$$E_i = m_0c^2.$$

Therefore the original bombarding energy must be

$$E_0 = 6m_0c^2 = 5630 \text{ Mev}.$$

The actual threshold is less than this, since nucleons in a target nucleus have appreciable internal motion. If the bombarded nucleon in a nucleus is momentarily headed opposite to the incoming proton, it will reduce the net momentum. In effect, the whole nucleus, instead of just the four protons emitted, helps to take up the bombarding momentum.

2. The hyperons ($\Lambda^0; \Sigma^+, \Sigma^0, \Sigma^-; \Xi^0, \Xi^-; \Omega^-$). The hyperons appear from their decays to be compounds of nucleons and mesons. However, since we still do not know why any of the particles have the masses they do, it may be that the stability of the lightest baryon, the proton, is accidental. Perhaps any one of the baryons is as fundamental as any other. The latest theoretical efforts have viewed all these particles as different states of the same basic object.

All the hyperons have negative strangeness; their antiparticles, of course, have positive strangeness. When the big accelerators first started producing them, they were always seen in association with K-mesons of positive strangeness. Now with available energies large enough to create antibaryons, the strangeness and baryon conservation laws can be satisfied by creation of hyperon pairs. For instance, Plate V shows one of the first examples of an anti-xi particle. The antiproton-proton collision in this case produced an xi pair.

The Plates containing bubble chamber pictures illustrate many of the production and decay processes of the hyperons. It would be almost impossible to credit the discovery of any of these particles to one person. Most of them were theoretically postulated in 1956 by Gell-Mann and independently by Nishijima, in order to fit the organization scheme of the particle chart on pp. 32f. Before this, many of them had been seen, although not identified or understood, in cosmic ray work. Several, such as the anti-xi particles, have been deliberately sought in large collaborative efforts at the high energy accelerators.

In terms of isotopic spin there is a singlet (lambda); triplet (sigma); doublet (xi or cascade), and singlet (Ω^-). Because of their strangeness numbers, they must, with one exception, decay through the Weak Interaction. The exception is the Σ^0, which has an electromagnetic decay route open,

$$\Sigma^0 \rightarrow \Lambda^0 + \gamma.$$

Since both Σ^0 and Λ^0 have strangeness of -1, the process is allowed.
The xi has a strangeness number of -2. It does not decay directly to a nucleon, but has to go by a two-step process, first to Λ^0 and then to the nucleon. For this reason it was often referred to as "the Cascade particle." Apparently, the strangeness number can change by only one unit during the Weak Interaction. The particle which now deserves the cascade title is the Ω^-. It was discovered in February 1964 during a deliberate search using the huge 80-inch bubble chamber at Brookhaven Laboratory. The production process is

$$\underset{S=-1}{\mathrm{K^-}} + \underset{S=0}{\mathrm{p}} \rightarrow \underset{S=-3}{\Omega^-} + \underset{S=+1}{\mathrm{K^+}} + \underset{S=+1}{\overline{\mathrm{K^0}}}.$$

The Ω^- decays through the Weak Interaction either to a Ξ or a combination of Λ^0 and K^-.

Section 8.   The Resonances and Short-Lived Particles

Now we must face up to the limitations of our first organizational scheme. It does indeed emphasize some remarkable symmetries among the particles but many features are left unexplained. First of all, why are there only these particular particles, and can there be more? Secondly, although the rules we have specified do agree with the observations that have been made concerning which reactions go and which do not, the quantitative predictions are often poor or impossible to make. The search for high-energy reactions was started as a means of discovering the details of the nuclear force. The strong interaction can still not be described in detail, and we have come to realize that there is a class of Weak Interactions as well. The mechanism of the Weak Interaction is linked with the nature of the W-particle, and very likely has something to do with the existence of muon and electron, each with its own neutrino.

DETECTION METHODS FOR VERY SHORT-LIVED PARTICLES

Part of the answer as to whether or not there are undiscovered particles lies in the problem of detecting certain types of reactions. The particles whose existence we now know are linked together in a multitude of ways. If a route exists for the decay of a particle into a lighter one, then the decay will take place providing none of the conservation laws are violated. As we have seen, some of the interactions are not subject to some of the laws. The lambda hyperon, Λ^0, is coupled to its decay products of π^- and p^+ by the strong nuclear force. The decay would take place in about 10^{-23} sec except that this would not conserve strangeness. In a time of 2×10^{-10} sec, the Weak Interaction can finally cause the decay. This length of time is adequate to allow detection of the process with counters and track pictures. In the event shown in Plate XII, for example, the length of the Λ^0 path before decay was about 9 centimeters in the bubble chamber. For an average velocity close to the speed of light this corresponds to a lifetime of 3×10^{-10} sec. (The listed values in the table are all *rest half* lives. Experimental data must be corrected for relativistic time dilation.)

What happens if a particle can decay by a faster route? Consider, for example,

$$\underset{I=1}{\pi^0} \rightarrow \underset{I=0}{\gamma} + \underset{I=0}{\gamma} \qquad (t_{1/2} = 2.3 \times 10^{-16}\,\text{sec}),$$

and

$$\underset{I=1}{\Sigma^0} \rightarrow \underset{I=0}{\Lambda^0} + \underset{I=0}{\gamma} \qquad (t_{1/2} \ll 10^{-12}\,\text{sec}).$$

In these cases, the only conservation law violated is that of total isotopic spin. The decays take place through the electromagnetic interaction. To explain how this force can link electrically neutral particles to produce photons, we hypothesize the following double sequences:

$$\pi^0 \rightarrow \bar{p} + p \rightarrow \gamma + \gamma,$$

and

$$\Sigma^0 \rightarrow \bar{p} + p + \Lambda^0 \rightarrow \gamma + \Lambda^0.$$

The intermediate virtual steps can take place only in times short enough to satisfy Heisenberg's uncertainty relationship for the extra amount of mass-energy needed for the nucleon pair creation. Qualitatively this picture explains the very short lifetimes. A decay through the electromagnetic processes should take about 10^{-20} sec. The sequence through the virtual reactions will certainly slow things down, but exactly how much cannot be calculated with certainty since we still have no complete theory for the strong interactions which couple the mesons and the baryons.

In spite of the very short lifetimes, the π^0 and Σ^0 are easily detected by a special analysis. If we try the same measurement technique with the π^0 that we used with the Λ^0, the path length is just on the edge of observability. Taking the rest half life as a lower limit,

$$\text{path } \Delta x = tv = 0.7 \times 10^{-16} \times 3 \times 10^{10}\,\text{cm/sec} \approx 2 \times 10^{-6}\,\text{cm}.$$

Actual flight paths will be longer because of the relativistic effect. The grains of photographic emulsions cannot be made much smaller than 10^{-4} cm, and this is close to the limit of ordinary microscopic resolution. It would appear that measurement of the flight path for any *single* event is just beyond the limit of detectability.

In any of the interactions producing π^0-mesons, the actual detection depends on measuring the decay gammas or the electron pairs. Thus,

$$\pi^0 \to \gamma + \gamma,$$
$$\to \gamma + e^+ + e^- \quad (1\% \text{ of the time}).$$

Each γ will usually produce an electron pair, $\gamma \to e^- + e^+$. If the π^0 production and decay take place in a photographic emulsion, all that can be seen is the downstream appearance of one or both electron pairs produced by the decay gammas. It might seem that by the time evidence was visible in the form of electron tracks, the original event would be hopelessly lost. Nevertheless, it is possible to trace back enough of these V-shaped electron pairs to find the point of origin of the π^0's from which they came. The analysis of many such events yields statistical evidence for the very short half life of 0.7×10^{-16} sec.

This, however, is not the way the π^0 was discovered. Suppose π^--mesons of low energy are captured by hydrogen. There are two possible reactions,

$$\pi^- + p^+ \to n + \gamma,$$

and

$$\pi^- + p^+ \to n + \pi^0$$
$$ \hookrightarrow 2\gamma.$$

The problem now is to distinguish the γ's of one process from the γ's of the other process. There are, fortunately, very large differences. In the first case the entire mass-energy of the π^- goes to the γ, except for the small recoil energy of the neutron, and the 1.3 Mev difference between proton and neutron mass. In the second case this energy goes to the mass and kinetic energy of the π^0 which then divides it between the two gammas which are actually measured (Fig. 58).

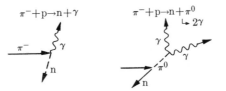

F<small>IG</small>. 58.   Difference between one- and two-photon production in π^--p capture at rest.

The two gammas will not have the same energy because the π^0 is recoiling from the neutron with about 4 Mev (the difference between the 5 Mev mass loss between π^- and π^0, and the 1 Mev gain required to change proton to neutron). As far as the π^0 is concerned, the two gammas go off in opposite directions, each taking half the energy (Fig. 59). In the laboratory, however, we must account for the appreciable momentum of the π^0. The gammas appear to be thrown off partly in the same direction, so that the original forward momentum

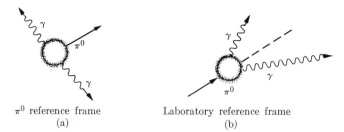

π^0 reference frame   Laboratory reference frame
(a)   (b)

Fig. 59. Energy of decay photons from π^0 in motion. (a) Gammas emitted opposite each other with equal energy. (b) Both gammas thrown forward with different energy due to different amount of Doppler shift.

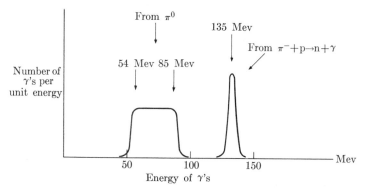

Fig. 60. Energy distribution of photons from π^--p capture.

of the π^0 is conserved. Since the π^0's are recoiling in all directions in our laboratory target, the gammas will be emitted in equal numbers in all directions. However, photons emitted from a moving source suffer a Doppler shift. For gamma rays of these energies we observe this as a change of energy. Instead of having all the gammas from the π^0 sequence come out with half the energy ($67\frac{1}{2}$ Mev), we will find a distribution of energies. The graph of Fig. 60 shows the energy spectrum which has been observed.

There is a uniform distribution of gammas versus energy between 54 Mev and 85 Mev. In spite of the small amount of kinetic energy left for the π^0 (less than 4 Mev) the conservation of momentum forces a spread of 31 Mev in the decay γ energies. Such a distribution is convincing evidence that the gammas do indeed come from the decay of a moving particle. The even distribution within the limits of maximum and minimum energy arises from the circumstance that the π^0's are being emitted uniformly in all directions, since the original π^-'s are captured at rest. The particular limits are related to the mass m_0 of the π^0 by the relationship

$$m_0 c^2 = 2\sqrt{E_1 E_2},$$

where E_1 is the minimum and E_2 the maximum gamma energy. If there had

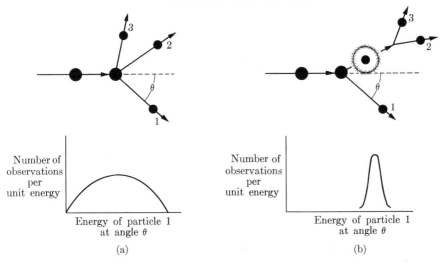

FIG. 61. Distribution of energies of particle emitted in two-body and three-body decay.

been no extra kinetic energy for the π^0, leaving it formed but at rest, the gammas would have been emitted uniformly in all directions still, but all of them would have half of the π^0 rest mass energy, $67\frac{1}{2}$ Mev. If the double gammas had been emitted from the primary reaction, there would have been yet a different distribution of energies. In such a case,

$$\pi^- + p^+ \to n + \gamma + \gamma.$$

The three particles left over would have an entirely different division of the energy compared with the actual reaction which has the intermediate π^0 step. Some gammas would take away almost the full energy of 135 Mev, leaving the other γ and the neutron with very little, and there would be other divisions leaving gammas with every energy from that maximum to zero.

This difference in the division of energy among the final products is the key to use in searching for other short-lived particles. How short a lifetime can we detect in this way? Consider a typical collision of two particles as seen in Fig. 61. The original reaction usually takes place through the strong nuclear forces in times of the order of 10^{-23} sec, long enough for a particle traveling close to the velocity of light to cross a nucleon diameter. In the diagram we propose two alternatives for the next step. In the first, three particles come out immediately, dividing up the energy and momentum so that both are conserved. Three-body interactions are usually complicated and produce distributions of energy for the participants that extend over wide ranges. The lighter objects will, on the average, take their equal share of momentum and therefore will usually take more than their share of kinetic energy. A typical distribution of the energy taken off by participant number (1) is shown in the diagram.

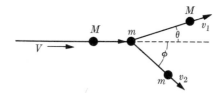

FIG. 62. Two-particle collision dynamics.

In the second case, there are the same three final products, but there is first an intermediate step involving just two bodies. Now, a two-body collision has very special properties. If one of the products goes off at any particular angle, then the momentum and energy it carries as well as the energy and angle of the second particle are *uniquely* determined. All this arises from the necessity of conserving momentum and energy.

In the more familiar nonrelativistic case, we write down the conservation laws for the reaction shown in Fig. 62 where the mass M and velocity V of the bombarding particle are known and it is assumed that the target mass m was originally at rest. In more complicated reactions in which several particles are emitted, the analysis must be done in three dimensions, which merely adds an extra equation.

Conservation of momentum in x-direction: $MV = Mv_1 \cos \theta + mv_2 \cos \phi$

Conservation of momentum in y-direction: $0 = Mv_1 \sin \theta - mv_2 \sin \phi$

Conservation of kinetic energy: $\tfrac{1}{2}MV^2 = \tfrac{1}{2}Mv_1^2 + \tfrac{1}{2}mv_2^2$

There are three equations and four unknowns: v_1 and θ the velocity and angle of the first particle; and v_2 and ϕ the velocity and angle of the second one. If one of these unknowns is determined by experimental choice, for instance, the angle of emission of the first particle, then the equations are completely determinate and no further choice is possible. If we choose to examine only those reactions where M has $\theta = 30°$, then the velocity of M at that angle will always be a certain value and the other particle, m, must travel at a particular angle ϕ with a particular velocity. This situation holds also for relativistic cases and for reactions where the two resulting particles may be different (and so have different masses) from the original two.

For the duration of the intermediate step, at least, this two-body interaction of Fig. 61(b) is radically different from the three-body decay. Now suppose that one of the two particles decays, turning the whole event into a three-body affair. Much of the strict organization still remains. Particle (1) continues on its way with its energy-momentum uniquely determined for that particular angle. The two decay products now have a very definite amount of energy to share between them, the rest mass of their parent plus the definite kinetic energy that it had at that particular angle. Figure 61(b) shows a typical distribution of energies for particle (1) at a particular angle. It is, of course, a line spectrum, centered around one particular energy. The width can be caused by experimental conditions, but there can also be a spread of energy for a more fundamental reason.

We have assumed that in the second case there is a clean break of the two particles before one of them decays. Energy and momentum are required to be conserved first for the intermediate process and then, independently, for the final decay. This decay takes place beyond the influence of particle (1). The problem is, how far away must the second particle be to get beyond this influence? It must certainly be beyond the range of the nuclear force -10^{-13} cm, but this can be a fuzzy range because of the Heisenberg uncertainty relationship. To the extent that we nail down the precise momentum of the two particles, their position is not so precise. Or to look at the situation another way, the shorter the lifetime of this intermediate process, the more uncertain will be the energy of the participants. As a rule of thumb, we can suggest that the lifetime before the second decay should be at least 10^{-22} sec if the participants are to be separate agents.

DISCOVERY OF THE PARTICLES UNSTABLE AGAINST STRONG NUCLEAR DECAY

Whether or not such intermediate events should be called particles is not so clear. Similar organization of energy distributions can occur in the decay of excited states of well-established particles. It has been apparent for many years that the nucleons are complex particles. For some purposes they can be described in terms of a core surrounded by clouds of mesons. Such a structure might have temporary excited states even as the complex atom can have its components arranged in unstable configurations. For the atom we picture the electron raised in energy to a distance further removed from the nucleus than normal and then dropping back with the emission of a photon (Fig. 63). During the 1950's evidence accumulated that the pion clouds of the nucleon might be arranged in abnormal ways in a collision, settling back into place with the emission of a meson. This could explain the resonance observed in pion scattering against protons which is shown in Fig. 51. Whenever a bombarding particle has just the right energy to lift a complex system to one of its excited states, the probability of the interaction will be very high. Presumably this is what happens when the π bombarding energy is just under 200 Mev.

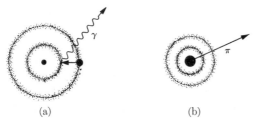

(a)   (b)

FIG. 63. (a) Excited Bohr atom returning to stable state with photon emission. (b) Excited nucleon can decay to stable configuration with π-emission.

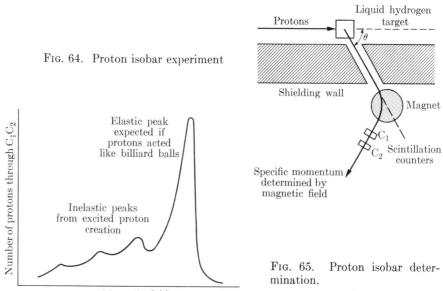

Fig. 64.   Proton isobar experiment

Fig. 65.   Proton isobar determination.

The most straightforward way of seeing these excited states is by bombarding the nucleon and observing the recoils. In proton-proton scattering, we should have a particularly simple case of two-body collision. Although the kinetic description must be relativistic at these energies, the conclusions concerning the unique energy of a particular particle at a particular angle are still valid. Figure 64 shows the experimental arrangement. At a particular angle from the bombarding direction, protons are detected and their momentum analyzed by a magnet. For a given bombarding energy, the momentum at a particular angle must have a single value. The counters $C_1 C_2$ are left stationary but the magnetic field is slowly increased. At a particular value of magnetic field, particles with the appropriate momentum are curved into the counters. If the protons collide only elastically, like billiard balls, the recoil proton coming down the shielding channel at the set angle will register in the counters for only *one* value of magnetic field.

The results of such an experiment are shown in Fig. 65. There is indeed a peak in the curve at the particular momentum corresponding to the elastic scattering. But, at that particular angle, there are also protons which arrived with smaller momentum-energy. In fact, there appear to be several groups of these at preferred momenta. An experiment analogous to this was done over forty years ago by Frank and Hertz. In that case, however, the bombarding particles were electrons with energies of a few electron volts and the targets were atoms. A measurement of the energy of the scattered electrons would produce a curve much like that shown in Fig. 65. The interpretation is that the electrons bounce elastically off the atoms unless they can donate some energy to the structure. The atom, it appears, can accept energy only in discrete amounts, which lift the electronic structure to quantized levels. From the separation of these states of excitation, details of the atomic structure can be calculated.

We come to the same conclusion in these latter days about the proton. It must have structure which can be arranged in definite excited states. The lifetime of these must be long enough to allow the excited proton to travel beyond the influence of the other proton, creating for a short time a two-body reaction with simple angular-momentum relationships. If the newly created meson were emitted while the two protons were still within nuclear range of each other, any one of the three particles could have a large range of momenta at any particular angle.

The original conservation laws for the intermediate two-body process look just the same as before except that the mass of one of the outgoing protons is now greater by the amount of excitation. Since even the first state has 300 Mev extra, the increase in mass is appreciable. As far as the detected proton is concerned, a chunk of the available kinetic energy was removed, and thus its own momentum at the particular angle is less.

Each of these excited states can be assigned, experimentally, a definite set of identification parameters, mass, charge, spin, strangeness, etc. For instance, what appears to be the first excited state of the nucleon has mass 1238 Mev; charge $+2$, $+1$, 0, or -1; spin $\frac{3}{2}\hbar$; isotopic spin $\frac{3}{2}$; strangeness zero. Whether or not we call these configurations *particles* is all a matter of what sort of experiment we are doing with them. They do indeed have a brief independent existence, but unlike the π^0, they are not even stable against decay through the strong nuclear interaction.

Since we have claimed that in one sense all the baryons may be parts of the same family, we should expect that all of the heavy particles may have excited states. As soon as large enough bombarding energies were available and this possibility became apparent, such states were found. Consider such a reaction as

$$\pi^- + p^+ \rightarrow \Lambda^0 + K^0 + \pi^0.$$

Could this perhaps have happened in the following way?

$$\pi^- + p^+ \rightarrow \Lambda^{0*} + K^0$$
$$ \hookrightarrow \Lambda^0 + \pi^0$$

The excited lambda decays to the normal lambda through the strong interaction and so cannot last more than a few times 10^{-23} sec. Since all the final particles are neutral until they in turn decay, how could we possibly decide between the two reactions? Even if the π were charged and had a visible track, the situation would not be clearer. For example,

$$\pi^- + n \rightarrow \Lambda^0 + K^0 + \pi^-, \quad \text{or} \quad \pi^- + n \rightarrow \Lambda^{0*} + K^0$$
$$\phantom{\pi^- + n \rightarrow \Lambda^0 + K^0 + \pi^-, \quad \text{or} \quad \pi^- + n \rightarrow} \hookrightarrow \Lambda^0 + \pi^-.$$

In either case the π-meson comes from the point of collision as closely as we can ever measure.

Once again we must appeal to the division of energy analysis. In the first case there is a three-body reaction and in the second case, only two share the energy originally. The mass of the excited Λ^0 can be calculated by measuring the momentum and angle of the K^0. This determines the mass of the other particle uniquely. If the analysis of many such events shows that the other "particle" has a range of masses, then the other particle was not single in the first place. What is observed, however, is that many of the other particles must indeed have a unique mass.

There has been no success in explaining nucleon structure in terms of a core surrounded by clouds of π- and K-mesons. By 1960, theorists were calling for other types of mesons.

The need to find such particles arose at just the time when high-speed computer analysis of bubble chamber tracks became possible. Consider a reaction such as

$$\pi^+ + p^+ \rightarrow p^+ + \pi^+ + \pi^+ + \pi^- + \pi^0.$$

At a bombarding energy of 1100 Mev, this process occurs frequently and was considered to be a simple case of multiple pion production. Could we be sure, however, that the reaction had not really occurred like this?

$$\pi^+ + p^+ \rightarrow p^+ + \eta^0 + \pi^+$$
$$\quad\quad\quad\quad \hookrightarrow \pi^0 + \pi^+ + \pi^-$$

The lifetime of the intermediate particle, η^0 (eta, zero), might be so short that all the π-mesons would appear to come from the same collision point. There is no longer the simple kinetics of a two-body reaction even if the η^0 does exist. It might seem that detection of such a transitory object would be hopeless, and indeed, if the necessary calculations could not be done rapidly on computers, the combination π's would probably remain unexplored.

The tentative assumption is made that each possible triplet (and for other explorations, each doublet) of mesons might have come from the decay of a single particle (Fig. 66). In our particular example, every event seen would have two possible triplets adding up to zero charge. The π^- and π^0 could be linked with either π^+. The total mass-energy of the intermediate parent is then known. It must be the sum of all the mass-energy of the triplet π's. Since its momentum must have given rise to the momenta of the three descendents, its velocity is known. Its rest mass, therefore, can be deduced from the known mass-energy. Now if the π's are merely emitted individually from the original reaction, this effective mass of the hypothetical particle can have a wide range of values, since there was no such particle. If it existed, however, taking off a definite chunk of mass from the original collision, then that unique mass value will appear in the analysis.

One obvious problem exists in the analysis of our particular example. We assumed that the total mass-energy and momentum of the intermediate particle could be found by summing the individual values for the three daughter pions. One of these, however, the π^0, is neutral and in most bubble chambers its decay

FIG. 66. Analysis of π triplet combinations in search for unique mass of hypothetical particle. Total mass-energy of compound particle $= E_1 + E_2 + E_3$. Total momentum of compound particle $= \mathbf{p}_1 + \mathbf{p}_2 + \mathbf{p}_3$. Rest mass of hypothetical compound particle can then be found from: $p = \sqrt{E^2 - (m_0c^2)^2}/c$.

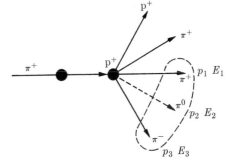

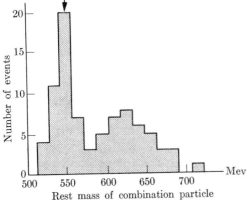

Rest mass of combination particle

FIG. 67. Typical plot of mass of combination particle composed of three π-mesons. If the transitory particle did not exist, a distribution of mass without peaks would be expected.

gammas would not produce electron pair tracks within the picture region. Still, the missing mass can be found. For instance, the total energy and momentum of the proton and one of the π^+ tracks can be measured. These must be equal to the original energy and momentum of the collision minus the mass energy and momentum of the hypothetical particle. Thus,

$$\pi^+ + p^+ \rightarrow \pi^+ + p^+ + (\pi^+ + \pi^- + \pi^0),$$
$$E_1 + E_2 = E_3 + E_4 + E_{\text{missing}},$$
$$\mathbf{p}_1 + \mathbf{p}_2 = \mathbf{p}_3 + \mathbf{p}_4 + \mathbf{p}_{\text{missing}},$$

where $\mathbf{p}$ denotes momentum.

Since we know the energy and momentum needed to complete the situation of the final state, we can find the missing mass of an intermediate particle, if it exists.

Many such combinations of multiple π production were analyzed starting in 1961, and a large number of short-lived particles have now been identified. Of course, if there are not many events to work with, statistics can produce strange results. In the preliminary work, several particles appeared which have since faded away. Figure 67 shows how the data appear when analyzed in the way we have described. It is easy to see how the chance absence of a particular configuration in a few events could lead to a dip in the curve and raise the possibility of the existence of yet another particle.

SIGNIFICANCE OF THE SHORT-LIVED PARTICLES

At the very beginning of the book we raised the problem of defining what we mean by "elementary" particle. For many purposes atoms can be considered to be fundamental, since they take part in chemical interactions as stable entities. However, we know how to operate on atoms in such a way that electrons and nuclei are isolated. Since these can have an independent existence, and since the atom can be described with almost complete accuracy in terms of the interaction of nucleus and electrons, we view the atom as a composite structure. To be sure, the atom is a little more than the sum of the obvious parts. Since the electrons are bound by the electromagnetic interaction, we can picture photons being interchanged among electrons and between electrons and nucleus. For the brief time allowed by the Heisenberg Uncertainty Principle, any of these photons might materialize into an electron pair, which would subtly alter the dynamics of the whole system. If the effect of this were great, simple calculations of electron energy states would be impossible. However, the electromagnetic interaction is indeed weak enough so that this transient mode produces only a small correction term in the energy level calculations.

From another point of view, however, we might justifiably identify each of the excited atomic states as a separate atom. The chemical properties are different from those of the stable system, and many of the identification parameters (mass-energy, spin, parity) are different. We usually do not think of these states as separate entities for two reasons. First of all, they are unstable against decay through the electromagnetic interaction. Secondly, and more important for our present considerations, the parameters of the ground state can be calculated without regard to those of the excited states. The interaction between them is weak enough so that the properties of one are barely influenced by the properties of the other.

Whether or not the neutron can be considered fundamental, and thus a particle in its own right, raises more complicated issues. It can be excited by bombardment to states that decay back to neutron and mesons. It is not even stable by itself, but decays through the Weak Interaction. Nevertheless, during its existence it has the attributes of a particle, definite amounts of mass, charge, spin, isotopic spin, hypercharge, and parity. In the chart on pp. 32f, we list the neutron along with all the other particles which are stable against fast decay through the strong nuclear interaction. Remembering our attitude toward excited states of atoms, one might be justified in claiming that all of the baryons including the neutron are merely excited states of the basic nucleon. Whether or not the nucleon is more basic than the others, simply because the proton is stable, remains to be considered. At least, looked at in this way, there appears to be no excuse for the arbitrary separation of particles into those which decay through the weak or electromagnetic interactions and those which we have thought of as resonances because they decay through the strong nuclear interaction.

We have been speaking of the interactions as if they were processes rather than forces. This is indeed the way calculations concerning them are performed.

Consider the particle combinations shown in Fig. 68. The neutron is responsive to all four interactions. We neglect gravity, because it is too weak, and consider the other routes by which the neutron could be connected with particle combinations having less mass than itself. The rule is that any system will transform into any other, providing that the two systems respond to the same interaction and that no conservation laws prohibit the change. If the change is to be permanent, the mass of the final system must be less than that of the original. Applying these rules, we see that the neutron is connected to the lighter proton by the strong nuclear interaction, which is portrayed as a route that is wide, corresponding to its strength. Of course, the neutron is also connected with the heavier proton, pi-meson system, but for the present we will consider only final states which have lower mass. The neutron cannot decay simply into a proton because of the law of conservation of charge. The strong nuclear route is blocked. The electromagnetic route is smaller by a factor of 100, but it can connect the neutron to a lighter combination of proton and electron. Charge would be conserved in this case, but leptons would not. This route cannot connect the neutron to a proton-electron-neutrino combination because neutrinos are not responsive to the electromagnetic interaction. The third route is narrower than the strong nuclear by a factor of 10^{13}, but it does connect without any prohibitions a combination responsive to the Weak Interaction. The narrowness of the route, the small energy difference between initial and final states, and the complexity of the three-body product all conspire to lengthen the decay time.

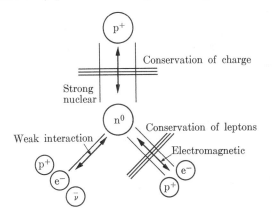

FIG. 68. Interactions viewed as routes between states.

Looked at in this way, the interactions lose their significance as forces. The Weak Interaction need not be considered a repulsive force, but simply another route by which particles can transform into each other. There is a somewhat analogous situation with chemical reactions which are best analyzed in terms of a dynamic equilibrium between two (or more) states. All of the interactions are two-way streets. If energy and the coincidence of geometry allow, the product particles can transform into the original state. We have seen an example of this in the neutrino detection experiment. An antineutrino captured by a

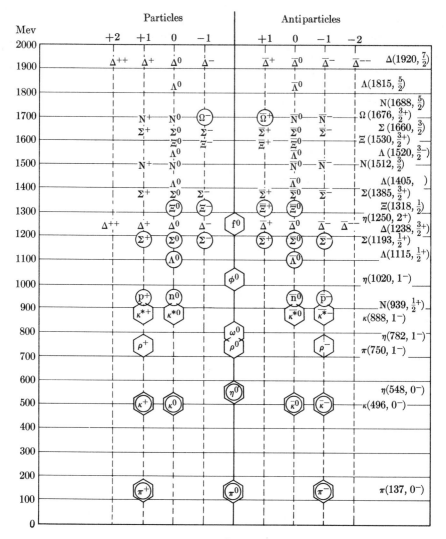

Fig. 69   Strongly interacting particles. ◯ signifies particles stable against nuclear decay; ⬡ signifies mesons; Δ (1,238, 3/2 +) → Generic type (mass in Mev, spin, parity). (Prepared by permission from an illustration copyrighted © 1964 by Scientific American, Inc. All rights reserved.)

proton produces a neutron and positron. In any such equilibrium reactions, a particle on one side of the transformation can be exchanged for the equivalent antiparticle on the other side.

In the diagram of neutron decay routes, we ignored interactions between the neutron and the particle combinations which have greater mass. Nature apparently does not ignore them, however. A satisfactory explanation for the electromagnetic decay of the neutral π^0-meson into two gammas involves a preliminary transition of the π^0 to a nucleon pair. The π^0 is connected to the nucleon pair and other baryon combinations by the strong nuclear interaction, but it is not affected by the electromagnetic interaction. The more massive nucleon pair can exist only for the brief time allowed by the Heisenberg Uncertainty Relationship. During this time, however, the nucleon pair can communicate with other particle combinations not only through the strong nuclear but also through the electromagnetic interaction. One of the communicating states is the two-gamma combination which satisfies energy conservation and so becomes a final product.

The operational question now arises as to whether the π^0 has a unique existence but occasionally must be treated as a nucleon pair, or whether the π^0 is no more than the sum of all the other combinations with which it can communicate through the strong nuclear interaction. Having raised the lid of this Pandora's box, we must also ask whether any of the particles responsive to the strong nuclear interaction have identities independent of the other particle combinations with which they can communicate. Perhaps the baryons and mesons are all creatures of each other and of the strong nuclear interaction.

Note that this model is meaningful in the case of the strong interaction, but would not be useful in describing systems bound by the weaker interactions. The ground state of an atom can be described independently of the excited states. Apparently this is not the case with the particles responsive to the nuclear interaction. There is no reason for considering one of the baryons as the ground state and the others as excited states, since no one of them can be described except in terms of the others. In this view of things, the proton is stable because, for some reason we do not yet understand, there is no baryon with a lower mass into which it can decay.

The interplay among baryons and mesons links together the existence of particles which can change into each other without violating any of the conservation laws which must be satisfied by the strong nuclear interaction. This suggests a new classification scheme based on groups whose members have the same b (baryon number), Y (hypercharge), and I (isotopic spin). The resonances, or particles unstable against strong nuclear decay, are members in good standing of such groups. The schemes in Figs. 69 and 70 are organized on this basis. They show, all the strongly interacting particles known in the spring of 1964. This organizing scheme is due to Geoffrey Chew, Murray Gell-Mann, and Arthur Rosenfeld and was presented in this form in *Scientific American*, February 1964. They propose a new naming system to avoid the confusion in the literature created by the discovery of so many new particles. The old name for the lowest lying member of a family with particular b, Y and I, is used for the whole family. The mass, spin, and parity of the member is then summarized in parentheses. For instance, the nucleon has $b = 1$, $Y = +1$, $I = \frac{1}{2}$. We call it N $(939, \frac{1}{2}^+)$. Two other doublets are in this family, N $(1512, \frac{3}{2})$ and N $(1688, \frac{5}{2})$. Presumably both of these have positive parity. Note that the first resonance seen, the so-called $\frac{3}{2}$, $\frac{3}{2}$ (spin, isotopic spin) resonance of the nucleon, is classed in a family called Δ (delta) with $b = 1$, $Y = 1$, $I = \frac{3}{2}$. Two of these quadruplets are

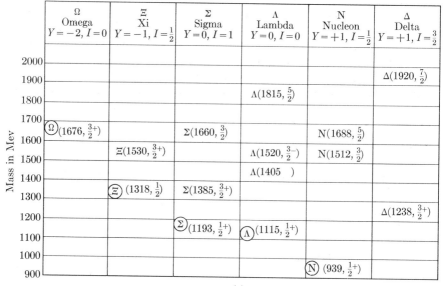

(a)

	Ω Omega $Y=-2, I=0$	Ξ Xi $Y=-1, I=\frac{1}{2}$	Σ Sigma $Y=0, I=1$	Λ Lambda $Y=0, I=0$	N Nucleon $Y=+1, I=\frac{1}{2}$	Δ Delta $Y=+1, I=\frac{3}{2}$
2000						
1900						$\Delta(1920, \frac{7}{2})$
1800				$\Lambda(1815, \frac{5}{2})$		
1700						
1600	$\Omega(1676, \frac{3}{2}+)$		$\Sigma(1660, \frac{3}{2})$		$N(1688, \frac{5}{2})$	
1500		$\Xi(1530, \frac{3}{2}+)$		$\Lambda(1520, \frac{3}{2}-)$	$N(1512, \frac{3}{2})$	
1400				$\Lambda(1405\ )$		
1300		$\Xi(1318, \frac{1}{2})$	$\Sigma(1385, \frac{3}{2}+)$			
1200						$\Delta(1238, \frac{3}{2}+)$
1100			$\Sigma(1193, \frac{1}{2}+)$	$\Lambda(1115, \frac{1}{2}+)$		
1000						
900					$N(939, \frac{1}{2}+)$	

(b)

	$\bar{\kappa}$ Antikappa $Y=-1, I=\frac{1}{2}$	π Pi $Y=0, I=1$	η Eta $Y=0, I=0$	κ Kappa $Y=+1, I=\frac{1}{2}$
1300				
1200			$\eta(1250, 2^+)$	
1100				
1000			$\eta(1020, 1^-)$	
900	$\bar{\kappa}(888, 1^-)$			$\kappa(888, 1^-)$
800				
700		$\pi(750, 1^-)$	$\eta(782, 1^-)$	
600				
500	$\bar{\kappa}(496, 0^-)$		$\eta(548, 0^-)$	$\kappa(496, 0^-)$
400				
300				
200				
100		$\pi(137, 0^-)$		
0				

Mass in Mev

FIG. 70. (a) Baryon multiplets grouped according to hypercharge Y and isotopic spin I. (b) Meson multiplets grouped according to hypercharge Y and isotopic spin I. (Prepared by permission from an illustration copyrighted © 1964 by Scientific American, Inc. All rights reserved.)

known, Δ (1238, $\frac{3}{2}^+$) and Δ (1920, $\frac{7}{2}$). The familiar π-meson with $b = 0$, $Y = 0$, $I = 1$, has another member called π (750, 1^-).

Suppose that we assume that any particle is made up of all the other particle combinations with which it can communicate through the strong nuclear interaction. (Note that this does not involve the leptons or the photon.) In a complete theory we should be able to show why these interacting systems appear with the particular properties we observe and no others. The mass of the nucleon, for instance, must have the value it does as a consequence of the dynamics of the interactions. Chew and Frautschi of the University of California refer to this situation as "bootstrap dynamics." No one has succeeded in calculating the properties of these particles as inevitable consequences of their strong interactions with each other, but it presents a fascinating challenge.

In the meantime, given the existing particles, new classification schemes have called for certain other particles. One of these schemes associates particles differing only in spin and mass, in analogy with an atomic system where each new angular momentum value is associated with a particular quantized energy state. According to this scheme, any known particle should have more massive counterparts with the same values of b, I and Y, but with spins differing by two units. The lines linking such particles on a graph of spin versus mass are known as Regge trajectories, after the man who first pointed out this possibility. Only three pairs of particles linked by these trajectories are now known, but others are being sought.

Another classification scheme, due to Gell-Mann and Ne'eman, emphasizes the fact that the differences of mass between baryons is small compared with their mass. For instance, the mass difference between nucleon and lambda is about 18% of the nucleon mass, and the difference between lambda and sigma is 8% of the lambda mass. If we were to assume that all the spin $\frac{1}{2}$ baryons are basically the same material, we might account for their mass separation in terms of their response to some interaction which arranges them in different states. In an analogous situation, particles with spin are separated into slightly different mass-energy states in the presence of a magnetic field. Similarly, the response of the electric charge of a particle to the electromagnetic field separates it into an isotopic spin multiplet whose members have slightly different masses. Perhaps there is a quantity or parameter which responds to some part of the strong nuclear interaction to form supermultiplets. (Perhaps the nuclear force must be described in terms of two or more interactions.) Because of the strength of the nuclear interaction, the mass separation might be as large as that observed.

Since the isotopic spin multiplets are different in electric charge, perhaps the supermultiplets could be different in hypercharge. We would group together particles having the same spin and parity, but differing in charge and hypercharge. Starting with the nucleons, with hypercharge Y of $+1$, a supermultiplet of this type would contain particles with $Y = 0$ and $Y = -1$. Our description of such a situation must contain terms accounting for the transformation of the system from one state to another. The transformations could

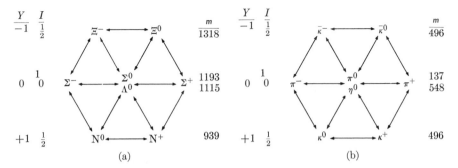

FIG. 71. Eightfold way arrangement of some particles stable against nuclear decay. (a) Baryon octet. (b) Meson octet. (Prepared by permission from an illustration copyrighted © 1964 by Scientific American, Inc. All rights reserved.)

occur with a change of charge, hypercharge, or the two together. A diagram of the baryon supermultiplet and the connecting transformations is shown in Fig. 71. Note that it is represented as a plot of hypercharge versus charge but it is also roughly a plot of mass versus charge. Transformations in charge along the horizontal axis make a difference of only about 1% in mass, but the mass differences produced by transformations in hypercharge are about 10 times larger.

The description of these relationships in terms of the Lie algebra of groups has been very successful. This algebra specifies the number of interactions possible within a group having a particular number of members and transformation properties. In particular, it allows predictions to be made about the relationships of mass differences of these multiplets and about the number of members to be expected within each super multiplet. In the case of the baryons of spin $\frac{1}{2}$, the algebra calls for eight members, as shown in Fig. 71(a), including the two neutral particles with hypercharge zero. These two, of course, differ in total isotopic spin. The predicted mass relationships are simple and agree very accurately with the measured values. For this particular group,

$$\tfrac{1}{2}(m_N + m_\Xi) = \tfrac{3}{4}m_\Lambda + \tfrac{1}{4}m_\Sigma.$$

The same octet pattern should be found for other strongly interacting particles with the same values of charge and hypercharge. The meson group of π, K, and η shown in Fig. 71(b), satisfies the relationship among masses, providing that the squares of the masses are used. This difference in the mass rule between mesons and baryons may be linked with the fact that the separation of masses for the mesons is as large as the masses themselves. The heavier and less stable resonance particles may also fall into similar patterns, as shown in Fig. 72 for the mesons, but the actual values of spin and parity for many of the baryons have not been measured.

Octets are not the only arrangement possible. The same relationships between isotopic spin and hypercharge change can also produce singlets and decuplets. In a decuplet of baryons, the mass difference between members of

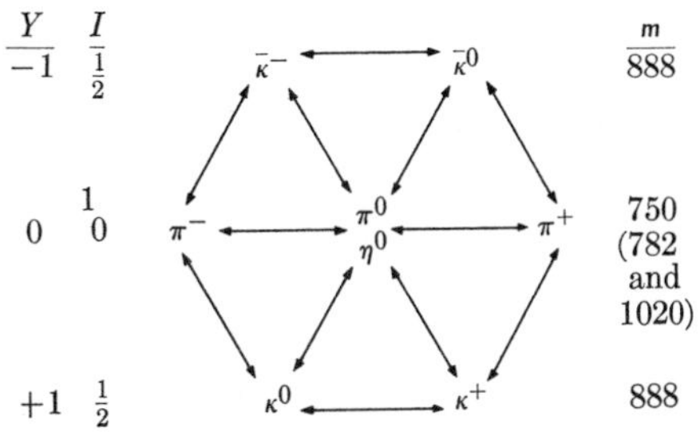

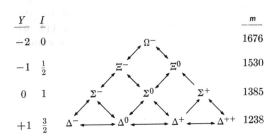

Fig. 72. Eightfold way prediction for some particles unstable against nuclear decay. The predicted value for the η^0 mass is 925 Mev. Instead, there are two η^0's with $Y = 0$ and $I = 0$. The 8-fold way can accommodate this situation.

Fig. 73. Eightfold way arrangement of a decuplet. Figures 72 and 73 are prepared by permission from an illustration copyrighted © 1964 by Scientific American, Inc. All rights reserved.

adjacent hypercharge should be equal. The arrangement is shown in Fig. 73. In this scheme, the first resonance to be discovered (the $\frac{3}{2}$ spin, $\frac{3}{2}$ isotopic spin proton, pion resonance) forms the base. Its isotopic spin of $\frac{3}{2}$ produces four charge possibilities. Enough of the other particles in the decuplet were known in 1963 to allow predictions of the mass and other parameters of the missing members. In particular, there should be a singlet with hypercharge of -2 (strangeness -3) and mass of 1676 Mev, which would be stable against strong nuclear decay. This is the Ω^- which was discovered in 1964.

The particular algebra which permitted these predictions is known as SU(3). The symbols stand for Special Unitary group for 3×3 arrays. The special condition eliminates one of the nine components, leaving only eight independent ones. Three of these are associated with isotopic spin orientations, one with hypercharge, two with transformations between states with adjacent hypercharge, and two with transformations between states with adjacent hypercharge and electric charge. The system has been known as The Eightfold Way.

There may be other arrangements which encompass all of the particles and include the present organizational schemes as special cases. One possibility is that all the strongly interacting particles are manifestations of three more primitive ones. These have been called the "Quark." Among other strange features, they would have fractional electric charge.

At the beginning of this book, we reviewed several classification schemes that had been significant in the development of science. The problem of successful classification has always been to choose the right parameter. This problem has been dramatically forced upon us during the years of particle research since 1950. The parameters of isotopic spin, hypercharge, and parity have been measured and assigned to the particles, but more important has been the change of attitude toward these assignments. The organization schemes are now more concerned with the relationships among particles than with the particles themselves.

Some of the problems, perhaps the crucial ones, will not be solved until we can use the next generation of accelerators which will have energies ten times those now available. Hopefully, we will find that the weak interactions can indeed be explained in terms of one Weak Interaction and that the strong nuclear force (or forces) can account for the multiple manifestations of a very small number of primitive particles. Perhaps it can account for all of the strongly interacting particles without any one of them being more primitive than the others. We may find that the W-particle (or particles) can account for the existence of the heavy electron known as the muon. And more surely yet, we may expect that new problems will arise whose fundamental nature we cannot now even surmise.

Appendixes

A–I HIGH-ENERGY ACCELERATORS

The production of mesons and the strange particles requires bombarding energies greater than 200 Mev. Accelerators for this energy range are the synchro-cyclotron and synchrotron, soon to be joined by a multi-Bev linear accelerator at Stanford in California. A list of the big machines now in use or being built is given in Fig. I–1.

All of these machines escort groups of protons or electrons from one accelerating stage to the next. There must therefore be an intrinsic mechanism to provide phase stability for a particle within its group. If a particle gets ahead of its group or falls behind, the dynamics of the machine must bring it back again. As in any focusing scheme, the restoring force must be roughly proportional to the displacement. The oscillations about the equilibrium phase are often called *synchrotron oscillations*. The frequency of such phase oscillations is low compared with the frequency with which the group passes through the accelerating stages. At the 3 Bev proton synchrotron at Brookhaven Laboratory, the synchrotron oscillations have a frequency of several kilocycles while the frequency of passing the accelerating stage changes from 370 kc to 4.2 Mc.

All accelerators must provide stability against loss of particles from the assigned beam path. Consider, for instance, that the acceleration time is often as long as one second. During this time, the particles would fall 16 ft if there were no focusing forces preventing vertical movement. Actually, the gravitational force is negligible compared with errors in the electromagnetic forces of the guiding system. Because of the geometry of the big circular machines, the stray movements can usually be resolved into vertical and horizontal deviations. Focusing forces proportional to the displacement must be provided to restore a particle to the equilibrium orbit. The particles execute both vertical and horizontal oscillations about the equilibrium orbit with frequencies close to that of the revolution frequency. If either of these frequencies equals the other or the revolution frequency or a low harmonic of one of them, energy will be fed into that oscillation, increasing the amplitude until the beam "blows up" on the guide walls.

The accelerators can be analyzed in two stages. First is the gross description of how the group of particles is guided so as to synchronize it with the accelerating stages. The problems involved concern relativistic increase of mass and the programmed changes of orbit, guide field, and accelerating frequency. The second involves the more complex problem of providing continuous focusing conditions for phase and for horizontal and vertical displacements from the equilibrium orbit.

Synchro-Cyclotrons

Berkeley, California	730 Mev
Chicago, Illinois	460 Mev
Pittsburgh, Pennsylvania (Carnegie)	440 Mev
Nevis, New York (Columbia)	385 Mev
Dubna, USSR	680 Mev
Geneva, Switzerland (CERN)	600 Mev
Liverpool, England	400 Mev

Proton Synchrotrons

Brookhaven National Laboratory, New York	33 Bev	Alternating gradient
Argonne, Illinois	12.5 Bev	Zero gradient
Berkeley, California	6.2 Bev	
Brookhaven National Laboratory, New York	3.0 Bev	
Princeton, New Jersey	3.0 Bev	
Geneva, Switzerland	30 Bev	Alternating gradient
Saclay, France	3 Bev	
Delft, Netherlands	1 Bev	
Birmingham, England	1 Bev	
Harwell, England	7 Bev	
Dubna, USSR	10 Bev	
Moscow, USSR	7 Bev	Alternating gradient

Electron Synchrotrons

Cambridge, Massachusetts (Harvard, MIT)	6 Bev
Ithaca, New York (Cornell)	1.5 Bev
Pasadena, California (Cal. Tech)	1.2 Bev
Hamburg, Germany	7.5 Bev
Rome, Italy	1.2 Bev
Tokyo, Japan	1.3 Bev
Lund, Sweden	1.2 Bev

Electron Linear Accelerators

Stanford, California	1 Bev
Orsay, France	1 Bev
Kharkov, USSR	1 Bev

FIG. I–1.   Accelerators above 300 Mev.

Magnet (field perpendicular to paper)

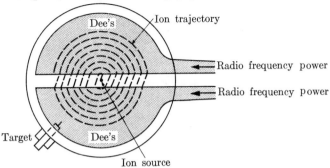

Fig. I-2. Cyclotron orbits.

In the nonrelativistic approximation, the revolution frequency of a particle in a uniform magnetic field is independent of its kinetic energy. As the particle is given energy by the acceleration system, it goes faster, experiencing a magnetic deflection force proportional to the velocity. The centripetal acceleration needed is proportional to the square of the velocity,

$$\frac{mv^2}{r} = Bqv \qquad \text{or} \qquad m\omega^2 r = Bq\omega r.$$

In these equations, m is the mass of the accelerating particle, v is the linear velocity, ω is the angular velocity, q is the charge, r is the radius of revolution, and B is the magnetic field. The angular velocity is therefore independent of the radius. In the cyclotron, the particles are released in the center of a uniform magnetic field region (Fig. I–2). A group of them is given electrostatic acceleration across a gap between two halves (called dee's) of a split metal cage. The two halves are driven with a powerful radio oscillator, oscillating positive and negative. Inside the half cages, the particles are not affected by the changing electric field. If the particle group orbits at the same frequency as the driven cages, it will once again be accelerated across the gap. The orbit radius increases at each crossing, and the particles themselves oscillate about the equilibrium position on the expanding orbit.

Above 10 Mev for protons, the relativistic increase in mass begins to ruin the synchronization of revolution frequency and oscillator frequency. Increase of B toward the outside of the magnet would appear at first to be a satisfactory escape. However, the second stage analysis of cyclotron operation requires that B steadily decrease toward the outside to provide the necessary focusing. The synchro-cyclotron was the answer to this problem. The driving oscillator is frequency modulated mechanically at a rate of several hundred sweeps per second. The frequency starts at the appropriate high frequency for low-energy particles near the center of the machine. A group of the bunches is then escorted by gradually decreasing the frequency as the group spirals to the outside and the particle energy and mass increase.

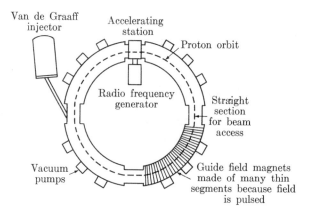

Fig. I-3. Plan view of the 3 Bev Cosmotron at Brookhaven Laboratory.

The energy of the particles depends on the radius of the magnetic guide field, at relativistic energies becoming proportional to the radius. Large accelerators therefore are evidently needed for the production of high-energy particles. It becomes impractical to build magnetic field areas with diameters much larger than five meters, which for protons means an energy of about 700 Mev. The next step up in energy is taken with the synchrotrons, which have been built for both electron and proton acceleration (Fig. I-3). Here the magnetic guide field is in the form of a race track, established by a train of separate magnets. This leaves the center of the region free of magnetic field. The particles now can make only small excursions about a set orbit. The magnetic field must be weak when the particles are first injected, so that the orbital forces are appropriate to that particular energy. Then the magnetic field must steadily increase as the particle energy increases. Meanwhile, the frequency of the acceleration stages must increase to keep up with the increasing revolution frequency of the particles. These acceleration stages usually provide several thousand electron volts to the particles during each passage. For acceleration into the Bev region, several million revolutions are thus required.

The detailed shape of the guide field is critical for a beam going around a machine that many times. Small errors could rapidly build into large oscillations, unless the field is designed to provide appropriate focusing. In the machines which accelerate protons to energies of 1 to 10 Bev, these focusing forces are relatively weak, and the vacuum chamber must be large in order to contain sizable oscillations. The cross section of the Cosmotron vacuum tank, for instance, is 30″ wide by 6″ high. Since this must fit into the jaws of a magnet, the magnets and all their supplies must be very large. In 1953 a strong focusing system was discovered which allows only small-particle oscillations and therefore requires a smaller cross section for vacuum tank and magnet. With the size and cost per cross section greatly reduced, it became feasible to build the giant machines at Brookhaven and CERN in Geneva. These are called alter-

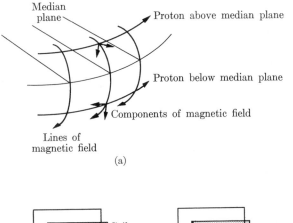

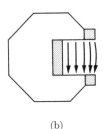

(a)   (b)

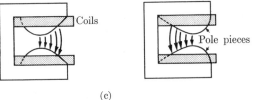

(c)

FIG. I-4. Focusing conditions which make possible the construction of larger accelerators, because they can have smaller cross sections. (a) The vertical component of the magnetic field forces the protons to follow the required circular orbit. The horizontal component of the magnetic field forces a proton up or down. In this case, a proton above the median plane would be forced down, and one below the median plane would be forced back up. Each proton oscillates up and down in a motion independent from its orbital motion. It also has a similar independent radial oscillation. (b) Weak focusing magnetic lines of force are almost parallel and almost vertical because field falls off very slowly toward outside edge. (c) Alternating gradient. Magnetic lines of force are highly curved because the field varies rapidly from inner to outer edge. The first field provides strong vertical focusing, but defocuses horizontally. It must be followed by the second type of magnet which does just the opposite. The net result is an overall strong focusing.

nating gradient synchrotrons (AGS) because of the shape of the guide fields. Instead of having the magnetic field fall off gradually with radius, so that the field is almost uniform, the AGS machines contain pole pieces which provide magnetic fields which vary rapidly with radius. Such a field provides focusing in one dimension but defocusing in the other. A series of alternating regions with the field first stronger toward the inside and weaker toward larger radius, and then vice versa, provides strong focusing both vertically and horizontally. The focusing conditions are illustrated in Fig. I-4. Preliminary designs have been made for a machine of this type which would accelerate protons to 1000 Bev. It would cost about 10^9 dollars and would have a circumference of about 18 mi. In 1963 a president's advisory commission urged that the detailed design study for such a machine be started immediately.

A–II   PARTICLE DETECTION

The energy involved in the passage of a single particle through a detection system is usually smaller than that needed for the gross operation of electric lights by a factor of 10^{12}. The affected regions are ten thousand times smaller in linear dimension than the minimum required for microscopic detection. Obviously, all detection systems must have intrinsic amplification. In many detectors this is provided by an unstable condition which requires only a small additional threshold energy to trigger an avalanche of growth.

Ionization of the detector material is the primary act which starts most (though not all) detection sequences. The momentum transferred to a nearby atomic system by a passing charged particle is proportional to the time it spends in the vicinity, and therefore inversely proportional to the particle velocity. The *energy* lost to the system is therefore inversely proportional to the *square* of the velocity. As was pointed out in the analysis of the track pictures, the sparse thin trails are caused by high-velocity particles, while the thick trails are left by slow particles near the end of their range. Because of the relativistic speed limit, a minimum of ionization would be expected as the particles get close to the speed of light. However, the electric field of a relativistic particle as seen by the stationary atom is disk shaped with stronger field reaching out perpendicular to the direction of motion. This produces a stronger pull on the atom, so that the curve of ionization versus particle energy begins to rise again. Such curves are shown in Fig. II–1. The minimum occurs when the particles have $\beta = v/c$ of 0.97.

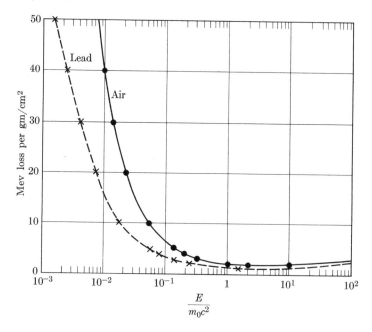

Fig. II-1. Energy loss of singly charged particle due to ionization as function of kinetic energy, measured in units of its rest mass.

The energy loss per centimeter is proportional to the square of the charge of the passing particle (since the momentum transfer is proportional to the charge). A precise calculation of energy loss must take into account the fact that deep-lying electrons in heavy atoms cannot take up small amounts of energy and that outer electrons shield inner ones from the field of the passing particle. As a first approximation, however, the energy loss per centimeter is proportional to the number of target electrons per volume of the material,

$$\frac{dE}{dx} \propto \frac{N_0}{A} Z\sigma.$$

The first term, N_0/A, Avogadro's number divided by the atomic weight of the material, is the number of atoms per gram. When multiplied by the atomic number, Z, this gives the number of electrons per gram. When multiplied by the density, σ, the result is the number of electrons per cubic centimeter. If both sides are divided by the density, we find that the energy loss per gm/cm^2 is proportional to the slowly varying ratio of Z/A. Two particular values are often useful for rough calculations. At minimum ionization, a singly charged particle loses 1.8 Mev/gm/cm^2 in air and 1.1 Mev/gm/cm^2 in lead.

Although most atoms have ionization potentials between 1 and 10 volts, the energy loss per ion pair formed in a gas is usually around 30 ev. Evidently most of this energy goes into atomic or molecular excitation which is dissipated in heat or light, and not into actual ionization. The precise value for any gas is critically dependent on the impurities present, so that handbook values may not apply to a particular experimental setup. In semiconductors, charge carriers are released into the conduction band with an average energy expenditure of only a couple of electron volts, yielding an intrinsic amplification advantage of 10 over a gas ionization detector.

Combining these figures of energy loss per gm/cm^2 and energy required per ion pair formed, we can analyze the required amplification for gas counter systems. At atmospheric pressure, the density of the common gases is about 10^{-3} gm/cm^3. Therefore in one centimeter, a fast minimum ionizing particle will lose about 2×10^3 ev and produce about 70 ion pairs. On a collection electrode, which for practical reasons cannot have a capacity of less than 10^{-11} farad (10 micromikes), this much charge will produce a voltage change of

$$\Delta V = \frac{70 \times 1.6 \times 10^{-19} \text{ coul}}{10^{-11} \text{ farad}} \approx 10^{-6} \text{ volt.}$$

Such a small signal is usually not detectable above the background noise. The old-fashioned, but still useful, Geiger counter amplifies this voltage by a factor of 10^6 to 10^7 in order to produce gross changes of lights or meter readings. The cylindrical geometry shown in Fig. II–2 is responsible for an electric field inversely proportional to the radial distance from the collection wire. Electrons released in the original ionization are pulled toward this central positive electrode, suffering constant collisions with the gas molecules in the chamber. As they approach the central wire, the stronger field gives them sufficient energy

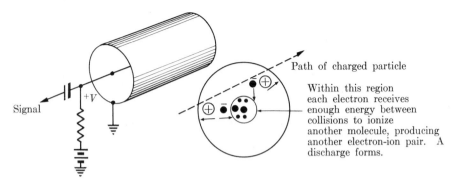

FIG. II-2. Geiger counter geometry.

in the dash between collisions to ionize the molecule they collide with. This is an avalanching process, since, from that point, each electron produced in the secondary ionizations will also gain sufficient energy to ionize the next atom with which it collides. An arc discharge is created in the region close to the wire. The electrons are collected in microsecond times, but the sheath of positive ions left around the wire drifts slowly toward the outer electrode. Under normal operating conditions this sheath quenches the reaction and keeps the counter insensitive for times of 10^{-4} to 10^{-3} sec.

New uses for old techniques seem to appear when they are most needed. The spark chamber, developed since 1960, makes use of ionization triggered arcs. In this case, however, it is the light produced that is detected, at least in the most common version. The noble gases efficiently turn their ionization energy into visible light. The usual geometry for these chambers consists of layers of plane parallel metal plates, separated by a few millimeters to a few centimeters of gas. Upon command of some other sensing device, the field across the gaps is abruptly raised for a few microseconds to about 10 thousand volts/cm. The ion trails left by a passing charged particle serve as leaders for the lightning discharges between the plates. Cameras observing between the gaps and at right angles to each other, record the spark trails. Spark chamber pictures are shown in Plates IX and XIII.

Many solids and liquids convert molecular excitation energy into visible light. Once again, this is the basis of an old technique of particle detection. The Geiger scattering experiments which led to the Rutherford nuclear atom were performed with scintillation detectors. A zinc sulfide screen, bombarded by the alpha particles, was monitored by eye. Now we have a variety of more convenient scintillating substances, and can monitor them with photomultiplier tubes. A typical counter arrangement is sketched in Fig. II–3. The efficiency of conversion of photons to electrons in the photosensitive surface of the tube is about 10%. In most experimental arrangements, only about 10% of the ionization energy lost is turned into photons which reach the photomultiplier. A minimum ionizing particle loses about 2 Mev going through a centimeter of plastic scintillator. Each photon requires about 2 ev. Considering the conversion efficiencies, this means a yield of 10^4 electrons starting down the multiplier

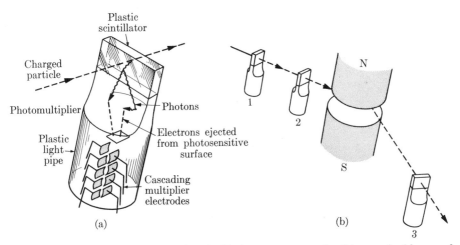

FIG. II-3. Particle detection with scintillation counters. In (b), a coincidence of counters 1, 2, 3 in sequence determines the trajectory of a charged particle with a specific curvature in the magnetic field.

chain. These tubes are operated with gains between 10^5 and 10^7. A pulse of 10^{10} electrons carries a charge of 10^{-9} coul which would produce a voltage change of 100 volts on a capacity of 10^{-11} farad. Many scintillators yield all their light in less than 10^{-7} sec, and most of it in about 10^{-8} sec. The photomultipliers add a spread of only a few times 10^{-9} sec. Consequently, for a period of 10^{-8} sec, there is an output current of 10^{-1} amp. In the usual arrangement, this flows through an impedance of 10^2 ohms to produce a signal of 10 volts at the end of a cable. Needless to say, in actual experiments the differences between these order-of-magnitude values and the actual ones reflect the skill of the experimenter and the existence of the latest commercial improvement. They may make the difference between success or failure of the experiment.

Another process, very different from scintillation, yields light during the passage of a charged particle. If the particle is traveling faster than the speed of light *in the material*, a bow wave cone of light is given off, called "Cerenkov radiation." From our mental picture of the electromagnetic effect which is being propagated by the virtual emission of photons, we must expect such an effect. If the particle which emits the photons is traveling faster than the photons can, some of them will be lost. The wave model explanation is illustrated in Fig. II-4. The peculiar relationship between angle of light emission and velocity of particle is sometimes used as a measure of particle velocity. Counters making use of the Cerenkov effect are built much like scintillation counters, with care taken that the Cerenkov radiation is not masked by any scintillating property of the detector. Since no light at all is produced unless β of the particle is greater than $1/n$, where n is the index of refraction of the material, Cerenkov counters have a built-in threshold discrimination. They are completely insensitive to low velocity background particles. Some detectors consist of variable pressure gas containers. The variable index of refraction provides variable threshold for the detection of particles of different velocities. Another feature of this phenomenon

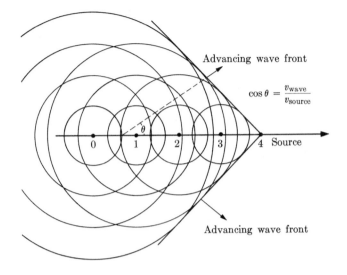

Fig. II-4. Cerenkov radiation. 0, 1, 2, 3, 4 are successive positions of charged particle. Wave velocity is 0.8 that of the source. The circles are the advancing wave crests. These add coherently along a wave front as shown. If the wave is light, traveling at a velocity c/n, where n is the index of refraction of the medium and the velocity of the charged particle is βc, $\cos \theta = 1/\beta n$.

is that the light is emitted only during the passage of the particle. Scintillation is a decay process of excited states and with most materials lasts at least ten times as long as a typical Cerenkov pulse.

Cloud chambers, bubble chambers, and photographic emulsions make use of unstable conditions to produce an amplification of the volume affected by ionization. In the case of the photographic emulsion, the primary ionization, whether by a photon or a charged particle, frees a silver atom from a silver iodide crystal. During the development procedure, the affected region of free silver grows 10^4 times in linear size and 10^{12} in volume. Since the original atomic dimension was 10^{-8} centimeter, this means that the developed silver grain is 10^{-4} centimeter in diameter. This is only twice the wavelength of visible light. Grain size in *ordinary* photographic film is usually ten times this size. Plate VI shows a track picture recorded in an emulsion.

The cloud and bubble chambers produce an even larger amplification. The vapor droplets or the bubbles are about 10^{-2} centimeter in diameter and thus are visible to the naked eye. In the cloud chamber a container of gas is saturated with a vapor, usually alcohol and water. A sudden volume expansion, produced by moving one wall of the chamber, drops the temperature about 20°C. The gas is then supersaturated. Over a considerable region of supersaturation, no droplets will form unless there are seed particles present in the gas. At the surface of an incipient droplet, the molecular dynamics are such that the evaporation is greater than the accumulation which is controlled by the vapor density and the molecular bonding related to surface tension. Beyond a critical size, a droplet will grow. This critical size is drastically reduced if the seed droplet has an electric charge. Thus if a charged particle leaves a trail of ions in its wake just at the moment of chamber expansion, a trail of droplets will grow. A strong light makes these easily visible to the eye or to recording cameras.

The explanation of the bubble chamber operation is much the same as for the cloud chamber. In this case, the volume of a liquid container is suddenly expanded, reducing the pressure. If the liquid was close to its boiling point, it will be hotter than its boiling point at this lower pressure, and bubbles will start forming. Bubble development is aided by the existence of some type of seed, such as dust or sharp points on surfaces. If ions have just been formed, the bubbles grow preferentially on them. An ion trail turns into a bubble trail, which is seen or photographed.

The peculiar advantage of the bubble chamber over the cloud chamber is one of greater density. High-energy particles have long interaction paths. To observe these effects in low-density cloud chambers, the chambers must be made very large and thus awkward to operate and photograph, or else barriers of solid materials must be inserted inside the chamber. The advantage in density, and so size, of a liquid over a gas is between 10^2 and 10^3. In practice, the bubble chambers are often easier to run than the cloud chambers, which are very sensitive to poisoning by small amounts of contamination. Furthermore, temperature equilibrium in a liquid chamber can be reestablished in a few seconds, whereas large cloud chambers often need recovery periods of up to a minute. To solve this latter problem, continuously sensitive cloud chambers have been used. In these devices, the supersaturation is caused by the diffusion of vapor from a heated region at the top of a container to a cooled region at the bottom. Tracks form in a sensitive region of supersaturation several centimeters deep in the middle.

The chambers and emulsions have historically been the instruments for discovery of complex events. Their space resolution and three-dimensional sensitivity are necessary virtues when the geometrical nature of an event is unknown. Their time resolution, however, is very poor. Although sometimes their sensitive time of 10^{-3} to 10^{-1} second is triggered by other sensing devices, frequently they merely record all events that take place during arbitrary intervals. For the discovery of rare events, hundreds of thousands of pictures may be scanned. Of course, in many cases, one good picture is very convincing. Counters, on the other hand, can be arranged to record all events of a particular type occurring in a particular geometry. Since the total recording time for a scintillation counter is less than 10^{-7} second, a million events may be analyzed in a few seconds without jamming.

The spark chamber combines space and time resolution in a compromise which has been exploited in many ingenious combinations for high-energy particle research. Since the high voltage across the plates is pulsed upon command, the chamber can passively ignore hundreds of thousands of particles which stream through. When the right combination is determined by counter arrays surrounding the chamber, the event can be captured with a sensitive time of about one microsecond.

A–III   BIBLIOGRAPHY

We list first the books about the microworld which are intended for the "intelligent layman." In most of these, it is assumed that the reader has had some high school science courses. The Science Study Series books are published by Doubleday.

The Neutron Story, Donald J. Hughes (Science Study Series, 1960)
The Restless Atom, Alfred Romer (Science Study Series, 1960)
Knowledge & Wonder, Victor Weisskopf (Science Study Series, 1962)
Inside the Atom, Isaac Asimov (Abelard-Schumann, New York, 1958)
Ultimate Particles of Matter, D. T. Lewis (Chantry Pub., London, 1959)
Cosmic View (*Universe in 40 Jumps*), K. Boeke (John Day Co., New York, 1957)

The following group demands more of the reader, although the material is well within the reach of anyone who has had a year of college physics.

Nuclear Physics and the Fundamental Particles, Heckman & Starring
(Holt, Rinehart & Winston, New York, 1963)
Elementary Particles, C. N. Yang (Princeton Univ. Press, 1962)
The World of Elementary Particles, K. W. Ford (Blaisdell, New York, 1963)
Elementary Particles, Thorndike & Frisch (Van Nostrand, Princeton, N.J., 1963)
Tracking Down Particles, R. D. Hill (Benjamin, New York, 1964)

Scientific American has had many articles on this subject:

The Overthrow of Parity	Philip Morrison	April	1957
Pions	Robert Marshak	Jan.	1957
Elementary Particles	Gell-Mann & Rosenbaum	July	1957
Principle of Uncertainty	George Gamow	Jan.	1958
Anti-Matter	Burbidge & Hoyle	April	1958
The Atomic Nucleus	R. E. Peierls	Jan.	1959
Ionizing Radiation	R. Platzman	Sept.	1959
Exclusion Principle	George Gamow	July	1959
High Energy Cosmic Rays	Bruno Rossi	Nov.	1959
The Weak Interactions	S. B. Treiman	March	1959
The Nuclear Force	R. Marshak	March	1960
Neutrino Astronomy	Philip Morrison	Aug.	1962
The Muon	Sheldon Penman	July	1961
Gravity	George Gamow	March	1961
Two Neutrino Experiment	Leon Lederman	March	1963
Hypernuclei	V. L. Telegdi	Jan.	1962
Strongly Interacting Particles	Chew, Gell-Mann, Rosenfeld	Feb.	1964

Advanced articles designed for the "intelligent physicist in another field" can be found in the annual review publications listed below. These are usually available in university libraries.

Annual Reviews of Nuclear Science, Annual Reviews Inc., Palo Alto, California
Progress in Elementary Particle and Cosmic Ray Physics, Interscience Publishers, Inc., New York.
Progress in Nuclear Physics, Pergamon Press, New York.

A–IV   TABLES

CONSTANTS AND USEFUL RELATIONSHIPS

Velocity of light	c	2.998×10^8 m/sec
Planck's constant	h	6.625×10^{-34} j·sec
Avogadro's number = mole	N	6.025×10^{23}
Quantized charge unit	e	1.602×10^{-19} coul
Electron rest mass	m_e	9.108×10^{-31} kg = 0.511 Mev
Proton rest mass	m_p	1.672×10^{-27} kg = 938 Mev
Boltzmann's constant	k	1.38×10^{-23} j/°K = 8.62×10^{-5} ev/°K
Electron volt	ev	1 ev = 1.6×10^{-19} joule

Magnetic field: 1 weber/m^2 = 10^4 gauss

　　　　Horizontal component of earth's field in New York $\approx \frac{1}{5}$ gauss

　　　　Large iron magnets saturate at $\approx$ 2 weber/m^2

Magnetic moment of electron $\mu_e = 5.79 \times 10^{-8}$ ev/gauss = 5.79×10^{-4} ev/weber/m^2

Momentum-wavelength: $p = \dfrac{h}{\lambda}$

Total energy $= E = mc^2 = \dfrac{m_0 c^2}{\sqrt{1 - v^2/c^2}} = \dfrac{m_0 c^2}{\sqrt{1 - \beta^2}}$

$$= m_0 c^2 + \tfrac{1}{2} m v^2 + \text{higher terms in } \frac{v}{c}$$

$$E^2 = c^2 p^2 + (m_0 c^2)^2$$

Time dilation: $\Delta t = \dfrac{\Delta t_0}{\sqrt{1 - \beta^2}}$

Heisenberg uncertainty relationships: $\Delta x \cdot \Delta p_x \geq \hbar \approx 1 \times 10^{-34}$ j·sec

$$\Delta \theta \cdot \Delta L \geq \hbar \approx 7 \times 10^{-16} \text{ ev·sec}$$

$$\Delta t \cdot \Delta E \geq \hbar \approx 7 \times 10^{-22} \text{ Mev·sec}$$

Exponential decay: $\Delta N = \lambda N \, \Delta t, \qquad N = N_0 e^{-\lambda t}$

$$T_{\text{mean life}} = \frac{1}{\lambda} = 1.45 T_{1/2 \text{ life}}$$

$$T_{1/2} = \frac{0.69}{\lambda}$$

Photon energy and momentum: $E = h\nu$

$$p = \frac{E}{c} = \frac{h\nu}{c} = \frac{h}{\lambda}$$

Compton effect wavelength change:

$$\lambda' - \lambda = \frac{h}{m_0 c} (1 - \cos \theta)$$

In usual scattering, m_0 is electron mass:

$$\lambda' - \lambda = 2.43 \times 10^{-12} \text{ meter } (1 - \cos \theta)$$

THE INTERACTIONS

Gravity
Gravitational "charge" is mass.
Gravitational force between particles negligible.
Force falls off with inverse square of distance, velocity independent, always attractive.
Graviton, agent of force, not detected.

Strong nuclear
Short range force.
Charge independent.
Strength of force when nucleons touch is over 100 times greater than electric force.

Electromagnetism
Charge (Q) quantized, either $+$ or $-$.
Agent of force is photon.
E-M force responsible for atomic and molecular binding, hence for most "forces" of everyday world.
Force is velocity dependent, changing aspect from electrostatic to electromagnetic depending on relative velocity of source and observer.
Force can be attractive or repulsive.

Weak interactions
10^{-13} times weaker than strong nuclear.
Responsible for β-decay radioactivity and particle decays taking longer than 10^{-15} sec.

THE RULES

The description of all interactions

Is independent of:	*Leading to conservation of:*
Space translation	Momentum
Time translation	Energy-Mass
Space rotation	Angular momentum
Zero of electric potential	Charge
Inversion of space and charge together	Product of space parity and charge reflection
Reversal of time	Time parity
?	Baryons and leptons

The strong and electromagnetic (but not the weak) interactions

Are independent of:	*Leading to conservation of:*
Reflection of space	Parity
Reflection of charge	Charge parity: I_3 and S

The strong (but not the electromagnetic or weak) interaction

Is independent of:	*Leading to conservation of:*
Charge	Isotopic spin, I

THE PARAMETERS

Spin s	In a magnetic field, a particle with spin s can exist in $(2s + 1)$ energy states.
Isotopic spin I	Interaction with the electromagnetic field separates particles with isotopic spin I into $(2I + 1)$ charged states.
Parity, even or odd	The function describing a particle system remains unchanged, except for a possible change of sign, if the sign of all the spatial coordinates is changed (space reflection). The function has odd parity if it changes sign: even if it does not.
Strangeness S	The charge centers of the isotopic spin multiplets within the same class are not the same. The "strangeness" number signifies the amount of this displacement. The charge centers for the two classes are chosen to be those for pions and nucleons.
Baryon and Lepton number $b \qquad\quad l$	The baryons have $b = +1$ for particles and $b = -1$ for antiparticles. The leptons have $l = +1$ for particles and $l = -1$ for antiparticles. For baryons and mesons electric charge $Q = \overset{+}{\underset{-}{0}}$ electron charge $$Q = e \left\lvert I_3 + \frac{b}{2} + \frac{S}{2} \right\rvert$$
Hypercharge Y	Y equals twice the average charge of a multiplet. $$Y = S + b$$

A–V   PROBLEMS

1. The force on a charged particle in an electric field is equal to qE. In a particular Millikan's apparatus, the field $E = 10^4$ volts/m. If an oil droplet contains one extra electron charge, and is just balanced in the electric and gravitation fields, what is its mass? What would be the approximate size of such a droplet? How accurately could the diameter of such a droplet be measured using visible light?

2. The average kinetic energy of a particle in thermal equilibrium is equal to $\frac{3}{2}kT$, where k is Boltzmann's constant and T is measured in degrees kelvin. Calculate the average energy in electron volts of a particle at room temperature. What temperature is necessary to produce particles with an average energy of 10^5 ev?

3. Perform an order-of-magnitude calculation to decide whether or not it is possible to weigh electrons. Assume reasonable dimensions and sensitivity for a pan balance. Decide what reasonable electrical capacity one pan might have. (10^{-10} farad?) How

much charge could be put on such a pan without producing electrical discharges to the supports? (Voltage as high as 10^5 volts?) How many electrons produce this much charge? How much would they weigh?

4. The nonrelativistic formula relating electromagnetic and centripetal force is: $Bev = mv^2/r$. If, in a cyclotron, $B = 1.5$ weber/m², what is the radius of curvature of the orbit of a 10 Mev proton?

5. Compute the rest mass of the electron, the proton, and one gram in electron volts.

6. The magnetic moment of the electron is 5.79×10^{-4} ev/weber/m². In a magnetic field of 10^4 gauss, what frequency radio signal will induce electron spin transitions?

7. The force exerted on a dipole in a nonhomogeneous field is: $F = \mu(dB/dy)$ where μ is the dipole moment, which can be thought of as the product of the charge strength and the length of the dipole, and dB/dy is the derivative of the field with respect to distance. (Demonstrate that this expression is correct.) If a magnetic field changes from 0.1 weber/m² to 2 weber/m² in 2 cm, what is the force exerted on an electron due to its magnetic moment? In a flight path of 1 meter through such an inhomogeneous field, what would be the vertical displacement if the velocity of the neutral atom is 10^4 m/sec?

8. Diagram the Bohr orbit positions and quantum numbers for the electrons of argon $(Z = 18)$.

9. What is the wavelength of a neutron which is in thermal equilibrium with molecules at room temperature? Compare with interatomic distances in a crystal.

10. What is $\beta(v/c)$ of a particle with relativistic mass equal to twice its rest mass?

11. If a beam of muons decays to $\frac{1}{2}$ intensity in 20 mi, what is the velocity and energy of each muon?

12. What is the uncertainty in momentum of a proton confined to a nucleus of 10^{-14} meter diameter? What uncertainty in energy does this imply?

13. How long can a π^0 exist as a nucleon pair without violating energy conservation?

14. From the definitions of strangeness and isotopic spin, show that the charge of the Ω singlet, with strangeness of -3, is -1. What is the charge of the Sigma Hyperon with $I_3 = -1$?

15. What is the probability that a thermal neutron will decay while passing through a detector 1 meter long?

16. Of 10^6 positive muons trapped in a detector, how many will live longer than 10 μsec? 100 μsec?

17. The mass of the earth is 6×10^{24} kg and the mass of the moon is 7×10^{22} kg. If equal amounts of positive charge accumulated on both, how much would be necessary to counteract completely the gravitational interaction?

18. Derive the Compton scattering formula, following the directions on p. 75. Calculate the "Compton wavelength" of the electron, h/m_0c.

19. To probe the structure of a nucleon whose diameter is about 3×10^{-15} meter, the wavelength of the probe must be smaller. If this is to be done with photons, what is the minimum energy necessary?

20. Would you expect that fission products are positive or negative beta emitters?

21. What is the velocity of an electron which has the same momentum as a visible light photon of 3 ev?

22. Devise possible production and decay schemes for the $\overline{\Omega}{}^+$.

23. In the two-body π-μ decay, the muon is given a unique energy of 4.5 Mev. What is the energy of the electron in the rare π-e decay?

24. If the π^0 has 4 Mev in the laboratory system, and then decays into two gammas, one in the forward direction and the other in the backward direction, what are the gamma energies?

25. Show a possible track picture of the production and subsequent decay of a Σ^0.

Index